OVER THE MOUNTAIN

SENIOR AUTHOR

JACK BOOTH

DAVID BOOTH

WILLA PAULI & JO PHENIX

IMPRESSIONS

HOLT, RINEHART AND WINSTON OF CANADA, LIMITED

Project Editor: Wendy Cochran
Developmental Editor: Diane Taylor
Production Editor: Jocelyn Van Huyse
Art Director: Wycliffe Smith
Cover Illustrator: Heather Cooper

ISBN: 0-03-921503-2

Canadian Cataloguing in Publication Data

Main entry under title:
Over the Mountain

(Impressions)
For use in schools.
ISBN 0-03-921503-2

1. Readers (Primary). 2. Readers–1950–
I. Booth, Jack, 1946–   II. Series.

PE1119.082 1985   428.6   C83-098252-3

Illustrations

Ken Stampnick: pp. 6-7; *Jenny Duda*: pp. 8-9, 10-11; *Bill Kimber*: pp. 12-18; *Carol Watson*: pp. 19-27, 28-38; *Jock MacRae*: p. 39; *Ann Blades*: pp. 40-53; *Laura Fernandez*: pp. 54-55, 196-207; *Marc Simont*: pp. 56-68; *Barbara Klunder*: pp. 69, 95, 96, 97, 98, 99, 100-107; *Margaret Hathaway*: pp. 70-81; *Brenda Clark*: pp. 82-88; *James Marshall*: pp. 89-94, 110-115; *Barb Griffin*: pp. 108-109; *Joanne Fitzgerald*: pp. 116-128; *Maurice Sendak*: pp. 129-135, 195; *Leslie Fairfield*: pp. 136-140; *San Murata*: pp. 141-145; *Clarence Porter*: pp. 146, 147, 148, 149, 150, 151; *Gerard Gauci*: pp. 152-153; *Wendy Wortsman*: pp. 154-155, *Carlo Italiano*: pp. 156-163; *Winnie Mertens*: pp. 164-169; *Bernadette Lau*: pp. 170-184; *Magda Markowski*: p. 185; *Chris Middleton*: pp. 186-194; *Terry Shoffner*: pp. 208-209; *Julian Mulock*: pp. 210-211, 212-222; *Pudlo Pudlat*: p. 223; *Veronika Martenova*: pp. 224-231; *Pitseolak*: pp. 232-237; *Ron Berg*: pp. 238-243; *Ted Harrison*: pp. 244-251; *Stephen Wilder*: p. 252; *Jonathon Prosky*: p. 253; *Alan Hicks*: p. 254; *Nyomina Park Elementary School*: p. 255; *Ann Norwick*: p. 256.

"Eagle Carrying Man" by Pudlo Pudlat: p. 223, a stonecut from the 1963 collection by the artist Pudlo Pudlat. Reproduced with the permission of the West Baffin Eskimo Co-operative Ltd., Cape Dorset, Northwest Territories.

"There's a Sound in the Sea—a Child's Eye View of the Whale": Collected by Tamar Griggs. Copyright © 1975 Tamar Griggs. Published by Scrimshaw Press, San Francisco, CA.

The authors and publishers gratefully acknowledge the consultants listed below for their contribution to the development of this program:

Isobel Bryan   *Primary Consultant   Ottawa Board of Education*
Ethel Buchanan   *Language Arts Consultant   Winnipeg ,Manitoba*
Heather Hayes   *Elementary Curriculum Consultant   City of Halifax Board of Education*
Gary Heck   *Curriculum Co-ordinator , Humanities   Lethbridge School District No. 51*
Ina Mary Rutherford   *Supervisor of Reading and Primary Instruction   Bruce County Board of Education*
Janice M. Sarkissian   *Supervisor of Instruction (Primary and Pre-School)   Greater Victoria School District*
Lynn Taylor   *Language Arts Consultant   Saskatoon Catholic School Board*

Printed in Canada   3 4 5   89 88 87 86

Acknowledgements

September: From SUNFLAKES AND SNOWSHINE by Newman and Boulanger. Reprinted by permission of Scholastic-TAB Publications. *An Animal Alphabet*: By Meguido Zola. © Meguido Zola. *Home Alone*: Text of HOME ALONE, copyright © 1979 by Eleanor Schick. Reprinted by permission of the publisher, Dial Books for Young Readers, A Division of E.P. Dutton, Inc. *One Snail and Me*: From ONE SNAIL AND ME by Emilie Warren McLeod. Copyright © 1961 by Emilie Warren McLeod. By permission of Little, Brown and Company in association with the Atlantic Monthly Press. *What to Name a Fish*: By Diane Suzana. Copyright © 1977 Suzana. *A Minnow*: By Gladys Nolan. By permission of Gladys Nolan. *A Salmon for Simon*: Text copyright © 1978 by Betty Waterton. Illustrations copyright © 1978 by Ann Blades. Reprinted with permission of the publisher, Douglas & McIntyre Ltd. *Nate the Great Goes Undercover*: Adaptation of NATE THE GREAT GOES UNDERCOVER by Marjorie Weinman Sharmat, illustrated by Marc Simont, text copyright © 1974 by Marjorie Weinman Sharmat, illustrations copyright © 1974 by Marc Simont. Reprinted by permission of Coward, McCann and Geoghegan. *Rattlesnake Skipping Song*: From ALLIGATOR PIE by Dennis Lee. Copyright © 1974 by Dennis Lee. Reprinted by permission of Macmillan of Canada, a Division of Gage Publishing Limited. *Ox-Cart Man*: By Donald Hall. Copyright © 1979 by Donald Hall. Originally published with illustrations by Barbara Cooney Porter. Reprinted by permission of Viking Penguin Inc. *There's a Party at Mona's Tonight*: Text and Illustrations from THERE'S A PARTY AT MONA'S TONIGHT by HARRY ALLARD. Copyright © 1981 by Harry Allard. Illustration copyright © 1981 by James Marshall. Reprinted by permission of Doubleday & Company, Inc. *Hallowe'en Poetry by Lilian Moore*: "I'm Skeleton," "Witch Goes Shopping," "No One," "Dear Country Witch," "Bedtime Stories," in SEE MY LOVELY POISON IVY. Copyright © 1975 Lilian Moore. Reprinted with the permission of Atheneum Publishers. *Old Devil Wind*: From OLD DEVIL WIND, Bill Martin, Jr. Copyright © 1970 by Holt, Rinehart and Winston. Used with permission. *Yummers*: By James Marshall. Copyright © 1973 by James Marshall. Reprinted by permission of Houghton Mifflin Company. *The Sandwich*: By Angela Wood and Ian Wallace. Copyright © 1975 by Ian Wallace and Angela Wood. Published by Kids Can Press, Toronto, Ontario. *Chicken Soup With Rice*: Complete text and art of CHICKEN SOUP WITH RICE: A Book of Months, written and illustrated by Maurice Sendak. Copyright © 1962 by Maurice Sendak. By permission of Harper & Row, Publishers, Inc. *The Surprise Sandwich*: By Red Lane. Reprinted by permission of Black Moss Press. *How Trouble Made the Monkey Eat Pepper*: By Rita Cox. Copyright © 1977 Rita Cox, Published by Kids Can Press, Toronto, Canada. *Street Song*: By Myra Cohn Livingston, in THE WAY THINGS ARE AND OTHER POEMS. Copyright © 1974 by Myra Cohn Livingston. A Margaret K. McElderry Book. Reprinted with the permission of Atheneum Publishers. *Apple War*: From CITY SANDWICH by Frank Asch. Copyright © 1978 by Frank Asch. By permission of Greenwillow Books (A Division of William Morrow). *My Mouth*: In EATS by Arnold Adoff. Copyright © 1979 by Arnold Adoff. By permission of Lothrop, Lee & Shepard Books (A Division of William Morrow & Company). *Revenge*: By Myra Cohn Livingston. From 4-WAY STOP AND OTHER POEMS by Myra Cohn Livingston. Copyright © 1976 by Myra Cohn Livingston. Reprinted by permission of Marian Reiner for the author. *Song of the Pop-Bottlers*: From A BOWL OF BISHOP by Morris Bishop. Copyright 1954 by Morris Bishop. A Dial Press Book, reprinted by permission of Doubleday & Company, Inc. *Where Seasons Change*: From SUNFLAKES AND SNOWSHINE by Newman and Boulanger. Reprinted by permission of Scholastic-TAB Publications. *My Feet Roll*: Illustrated by Winnie Mertons, 1977, Before We Are Six, Toronto. *How Six Found Christmas*: From HOW SIX FOUND CHRISTMAS by Trina Schart Hyman. Copyright © 1969 by Trina Schart Hyman. By permission of Little, Brown and Company. *Wishers*: By Dolores Hind. Reprinted by permission of Dolores Hind. *Do Not Open Until Christmas*: By Jean Little, reprinted from "SURPRISE." By permission of the author. *If I Want I Can Give It to a Friend*: (text and art) in I'LL BE YOU AND YOU BE ME by Ruth Krauss, pictures by Maurice Sendak. Text Copyright 1954 by Ruth Krauss. Pictures Copyright 1954 by Maurice Sendak. By permission of Harper & Row, Publishers, Inc. *A Wart Snake In a Fig Tree*: Text of A WART SNAKE IN A FIG TREE, copyright © 1968 by George Mendoza. Reprinted by permission of the publisher, Dial Books for Young Readers, A Division of E.P. Dutton, Inc. *Day and Night—How They Came To Be*: By Knud Rasmussen. Reprinted with permission of the heir, Rudolf Sand. *The Arctic—What Lives There*: Excerpt reprinted by permission of Coward, McCann & Geoghegan from THE ARCTIC AND THE ANTARCTIC: What Lives There, text copyright © 1975 by Lee Pennock Huntington. *Magic Words To Feel Better*: By Knud Rasmussen. Reprinted with permission of the heir, Rudolf Sand. *The Girl Who Became a Reindeer*: Adapted and reprinted from the original title, "The Boy Who Became a Reindeer" from THE DAY TUK BECAME A HUNTER AND OTHER ESKIMO STORIES, retold by Ronald Melzack. Copyright © 1967 by Ronald Melzack. Used by permission of The Canadian Publishers, McClelland and Stewart Limited, Toronto. *Pitseolak—Pictures Out of My Life*: From PITSEOLAK: PICTURES OUT OF MY LIFE, from recorded interviews by Dorothy Eber, Design Collaborative Books, Montreal. *A Gift For Kuni*: By Elizabeth Kastner. Reprinted from OWL Magazine with the permission of the publisher, The Young Naturalist Foundation. *There's A Sound in the Sea—a Child's Eye View of the Whale*: Collected by Tamar Griggs. Published by Scrimshaw Press.

The Girl Who Became a Reindeer: Adapted and reprinted by permission of DODD, MEAD & COMPANY, INC. from THE DAY TUK BECAME A HUNTER AND OTHER ESKIMO STORIES, retold by Ronald Melzack. © 1967 by Ronald Melzack.

Every reasonable effort has been made to trace the owners of copyrighted material and to make due acknowledgement. Any errors or omissions drawn to our attention will be gladly rectified in future editions.

Table of Contents

Now
by
Prince Redcloud

Close the barbecue.
Close the sun.
Close the home-run games we won.
Close the picnic.
Close the pool.
Close the summer.

Open school.

September
by
Fran Newman and Claudette Boulanger

There are pickles and peppers and pumpkins and piecrusts;
Butter and ice cream and cheeses to share.
There are hot dogs and french fries and soft drinks and candy—
    How soon will we get to the fair?

There are tractors and balers and combines and seeders;
Hunters and Belgians and ponies to spare.
There's quilting and weaving and candles and sewing—
    How far is it now to the fair?

There's roping and shearing and milking and riding;
Roses and asters and orchids so rare.
There's bingo and skill games and fun and excitement—
At last we've arrived at the fair!

An Animal Alphabet
by
Meguido Zola

Apes gibber.

Bees buzz.

Cattle low.

Doves coo.

Elephants trumpet.

Frogs croak.

Geese cackle.

Hyenas laugh.

Iguanas hiss.

Jackals howl.

Kiwi birds squawk.

Lions roar.

Monkeys chatter.

Nightingales warble.

Owls screech.

Puppies yelp.

Quails twitter.

Rabbits squeak.

Snakes rattle.

Tigers growl.

Umbrella birds chirp.

Vultures scream.

Wolves bay.

X-ray fish gurgle.

Yaks grunt.

Zebras bray.

gibber, buzz, low, coo, trumpet,
croak, cackle, laugh, hiss, howl,
squawk, roar, chatter, warble,
screech, yelp, twitter, squeak,
rattle, growl, chirp, scream,
bay, gurgle, grunt, bray

Home Alone
by
Eleanor Schick

I have walked home from school alone before.
I do that almost every day. But today it is different.
Today my mother started working all day.
That is why she will not be there when I get home from school.

I have my own keys.
The bigger key is for the downstairs door.
I have practised using them with Mom so I know how.

Some days after school I will be going to Scout meetings.
Some days I will be visiting with Tony or Jerry
or David. Some days I will be playing soccer
with the soccer team. Those days
Mom will pick me up on her way home
from work because I am not allowed
to walk home alone when it is dark.

But some days I will be coming right home
from school by myself. That's all right with me.

Mrs. Scott lives right next door.
She will be there if I need her for anything
or if I just get lonely and want to visit.
She hears me coming up the stairs,
and she opens the door to say hello.
She says she will be home all afternoon.

I have to lock the door when I come in
even before I call Bisquits. I promised Dad I would.

Next I call Mom at her office to say that I am home.
She is glad to hear that I locked the door right away.
I tell her I remember that if someone knocks,
I will not let them in. I will tell them,
"Mom is busy. Come back later."

Mom says there is a note on the bookcase in the hall.
She tells me she loves me, and she will be home
at six. I find the note. It says:

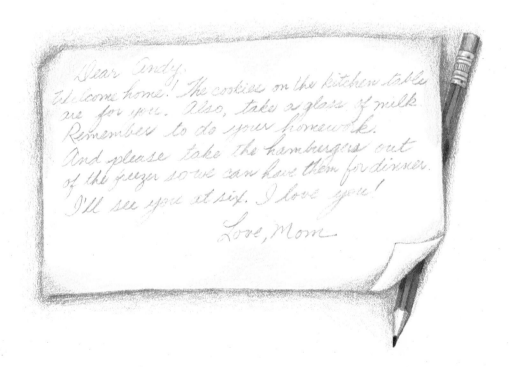

Dear Andy,
Welcome home! The cookies on the kitchen table
are for you. Also, take a glass of milk.
Remember to do your homework.
And please take the hamburgers out
of the freezer so we can have them for dinner.
I'll see you at six. I love you!
            Love, Mom

I fold the note and put it in my pocket.
I can look at it again to remember
all the things I have to do.

I hear footsteps on the stairs in the hall
outside our door. They sound louder
than they ever did before. Bisquits says
it is just someone coming home. The sound
of a key turning in a lock surprises me.
It is so loud, it sounds like someone
is opening our door. I look through the peephole
and see that it is just Mrs. Sherman
across the hall, coming home from shopping.
Bisquits says she knew that all the time.

The rooms are bigger when there is
no one here but Bisquits and me.
We walk through the house. It is very quiet.
The only sound is my footsteps. We go
into the kitchen. It is time to have cookies.
Bisquits is hungry too. Bisquits says
she is used to being home alone.
Sometimes she has to wait for us
all day, and she does not mind.
If Bisquits can stay home alone, then I can too.

I have even more friends besides Bisquits
who wait for me at home. They do not worry.
They know I will play with them when I get here.
Today I will build a town for them!
It will keep them warm and safe in the daytime
while they wait for me. I take my radio
off the night table. I put it in the middle of the town.

The animals gather around it. They think it is magic.
They say they like the music this town has
and they like the magic music box. Now
they do not have to hear the stairs creaking
in the hallway whenever someone comes home.
The tower has a clock so the animals can tell
what time it is. Right now they are helping me
watch for six o'clock.

A train drives into town. One of the cars
has cookies in it. The train is bringing cookies
to the animals. The animals are having a party
because they like the new town.

The phone rings. I say "Hello."
The lady asks for my mother.
I say, "My mother will call you back.
Can I take a message?" The lady says "Yes."
She spells out her name so I can write it down.
She tells me her phone number to write down too.
Then she thanks me and says "Good-bye."
Bisquits thinks I did that very well.

I put the note on the kitchen table
under the sugar bowl. I remember the hamburgers
and take them out of the freezer. I do
my last page of homework. I wash
the glass I used for milk.

Then I look out the window. The dark shadows
mean night is coming. Bisquits and I count
the lights in the windows across the street.
The animals are resting now. They had a good day.
Bisquits is cuddly. She likes our new town.
Bisquits says the animals hope we can keep
this town for a long time. Bisquits says
maybe Mom will not mind, if I promise
to keep my room very clean.

It is almost six o'clock. Mom gets home
even before she said she would!
I show Mom the town I built, with the clock
in the tower and the magic music box.

"It is beautiful," Mom says.

"Can I leave it up for a few days if I promise
to keep my room clean?" I ask.

"Yes," she says, "if you keep your promise."

I show her the note about Mrs. Franklin.
I show her the hamburgers defrosting
for dinner. Mom says I did a good job,
and she is very proud of me.

I tell her about the lemon seeds we planted
in school today and the candy dish
I am making out of clay.

Mom tells me about her new office. She says,
"It will look wonderful with a lemon plant
and a candy dish."

"And I will draw some pictures to put up
on your office walls!" I tell her.

Mom says, "That will make it just perfect!"

I set the table, while Mom starts cooking dinner.
"We'll have potatoes and a salad to go
with the hamburgers," she says.
"And there is still time, while dinner is cooking,
for you to take your bath," she tells me.

But first she lets me peek at the lemon cake
that she brought home for dessert.

One Snail and Me
by
Emilie Warren McLeod

There are things to do alone in a tub,
like being a fish and being a boat,
like bubbling and sloshing and chasing soap.
But it would be ever so much more fun
if done
by two or three or four.
Two whats? Three whats? Four or more whats?

Well, I do have a snail.
1 snail
makes a beautiful,
bubbly, silvery trail
on the edge of the tub.

And turtles, I have
2 turtles,
so bashful they won't leave their homes.
They blink and promise not to tell
that I am here without my shell.
One snail,
and me.

I have **3** ducks,
three Peking ducks.
They quack in mandarin Chinese
and swim with busy orange feet
around the island of my knees.
Two turtles,
one snail,
and me.

Better yet, I have
4 seals,
who juggle my soap on the tips of their tails
while unpacking the lunch
they brought in tin pails,
for three ducks,
two turtles,
one snail,
and me.

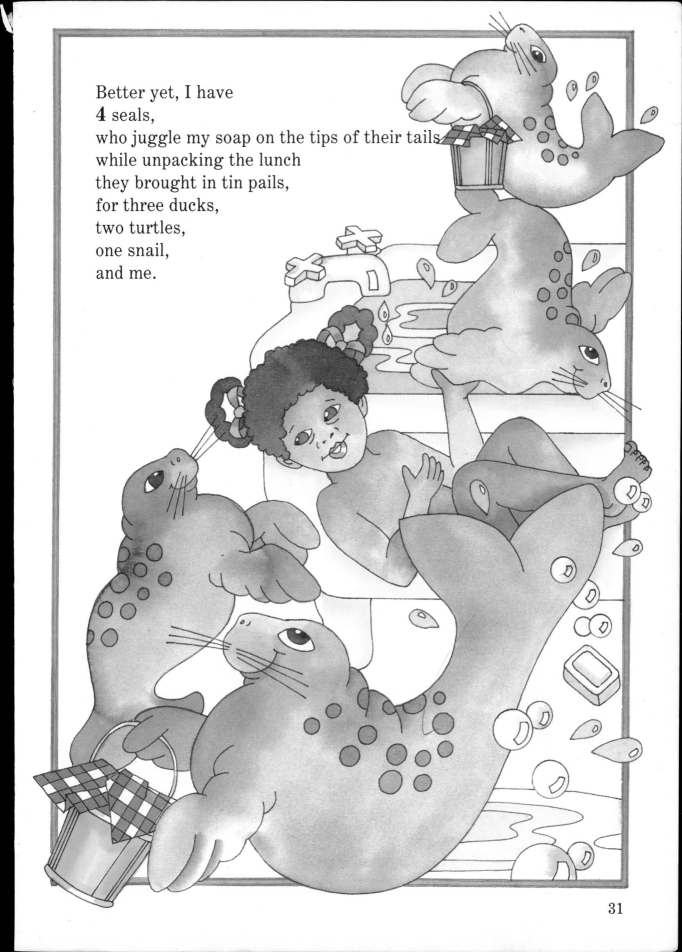

I have **5** whales,
five little whales
whose mother is lost.
They spout and pout
and flop about
with four seals,
three Peking ducks,
two turtles,
one snail,
and me.

And that's not all.
I have **6** kangaroos,
six girl kangaroos,
with a pocket each
filled with sand for a beach
and with red-striped
umbrellas and bathing shoes
for five little whales,
four seals,
three Peking ducks,
two turtles,
one snail,
and me.

I have **7** bears,
seven hungry bears.
They float on empty honey jars
while eating sticky candy bars
which they are very glad to share
with six kangaroos,
five small whales,
four seals,
three Peking ducks,
two turtles,
one snail,
and me.

And **8** alligators,
eight little alligators,
because the bigger ones
are people eaters
and we're not fond
of them at all—
the seven hungry honey bears,
six kangaroos,
five small whales,
four seals,
three ducks,
two turtles,
one snail,
and me.

I have **9** hippopotamuses—
or nine fine hippopotami—
of such tremendous heft
they take up all the tub that's left,
with most of them outside;
and eight alligators,
seven hungry bears,
six kangaroos,
five whales,
four seals,
three ducks,
two turtles,
one snail,
and me.

I have **10** little minnows who tickle,
ten little minnows with prickly fins,
who wriggle, and squiggle,
and tickle
the nine hippopotamuses,
eight alligators,
seven bears,
six kangaroos,
five whales,
four seals,
three ducks,
two turtles,
one snail,
and me.

We're all of a jumble
of splashes and bubbles,
of bathing shoes, beach sand,
of honey jars, lunch, and
giggles and tickles,
of water and soap.

We're all of a jumble
of me,
one snail,
two bashful turtles,
three Peking ducks,
four seals
with lunch in pails,
five little whales,
six kangaroos
with bathing shoes,
seven hungry bears,
eight alligators,
nine fine hippopotamuses,
and ten little minnows who tickle.

What to Name a Fish
by
Diane Suzana

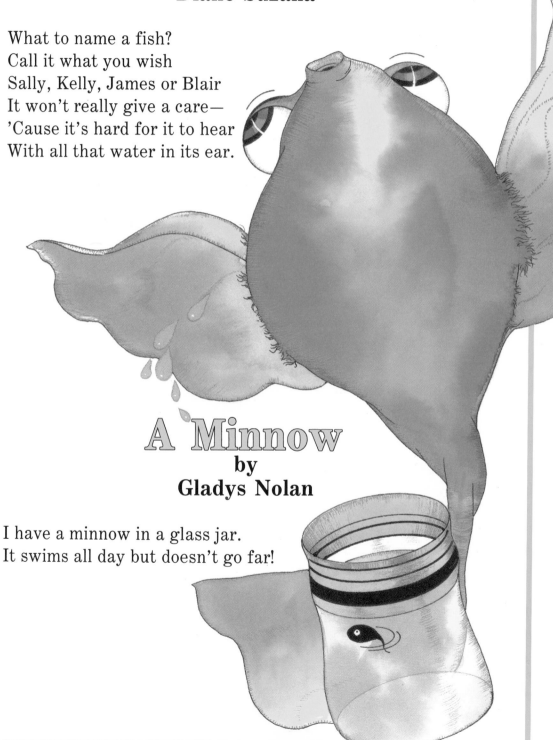

What to name a fish?
Call it what you wish
Sally, Kelly, James or Blair
It won't really give a care—
'Cause it's hard for it to hear
With all that water in its ear.

A Minnow
by
Gladys Nolan

I have a minnow in a glass jar.
It swims all day but doesn't go far!

A Salmon for Simon
by
Betty Waterton

All summer Simon had been fishing for salmon.

Last year, when he was little, his sisters had taught him
how to catch minnows with a strainer. But this year
his father had given him a fishing pole of his own,
and he had been fishing for a salmon every day.
He hadn't caught a single salmon.

Now it was September. It was that time of year
when many salmon were swimming past the island
where Simon lived, near the west coast of Canada.
They were returning from the sea, looking for the rivers
and little streams where they had been born.
There they would lay their eggs
so that more salmon could be born.

One day, when the tide was on its way out,
Simon and his two sisters went clam-digging.
As soon as their pail was full of clams,
his sisters took them home to their mother
to cook for supper, but Simon stayed at the beach.
He had his fishing pole with him,
as he had every day that summer.

"I'm going to stay and fish for a salmon," he thought.
And he did. He sat on a rock and fished.
He sat on a dock and fished.
But he didn't even see a salmon.

He stood on the edge of the beach and fished.
He saw red and purple starfish sticking to the rocks.
He saw small, green crabs scuttling among the seaweed.
He saw flat, white sand dollars lying on the wet sand.
He saw pink sea-anemones waving, pale jellyfish floating,
and shiners swimming. But he didn't see a salmon.

"Is it ever hard to catch a salmon," thought Simon.
He decided to stop fishing. Maybe forever.

Simon walked back along the beach to the place
where he and his sisters had been clam-digging.
The sea water had oozed up from the bottom of the hole
and filled it. Three seagulls sat beside it.
When Simon came near, they flew up into the air
crying *keer, keer, keer*.

"I'm not good at catching salmon,
but I am a good clam-digger," thought Simon.
He dug a few clams and put them on a nearby rock.
The gulls flew down, picked up the clams in their beaks,
carried them into the air and then dropped them.
The clams hit the rocks and broke open.

Simon listened to the *bang*, *bang*, *pop* of the clam shells
as they broke. He watched the gulls fly down
and eat the soft clams.

Then Simon heard something different.
Something sounding like FLAP, FLAP, FLAP.
"What's that?" he cried, but nobody answered.
He heard it again, FLAP, FLAP, FLAP,
and this time it was right above his head.
The seagulls flew off, calling *keer, keer, keer*.
Simon looked up—it was an eagle.

Its wings beat the air, FLAP, FLAP, FLAP,
as it climbed towards the treetops.
Simon had often seen bald eagles,
but this one was different, for it was carrying
something in its talons—something that glistened.

"A fish!" cried Simon, "he's got a fish!"
He was so excited that he began hopping about
and flapping his arms like eagles' wings.
The seagulls were excited too,
and they circled overhead, screeching.

In all the stir and confusion, the eagle dropped the fish.
Down it came out of the sky,
$$\text{down}$$
$$\text{down}$$
$$\text{down}$$
$$\text{down}$$
$$\text{down}$$

SPLAAT.........SPLASH
into the clam hole!

The fish lay on its side in the shallow water and did not move.
Simon ran over to it. "It's dead," he cried.
Suddenly the fish flicked its tail and flipped over
right side up. Its gills opened and closed and its fins
began to move slowly. "It's alive," shouted Simon.
Then he looked closer. His eyes grew round.
"It's alive and it's a salmon," he cried.
"It must be the most beautiful fish
in the world," thought Simon.

For it was a coho, or silver salmon,
which had come from far out in the Pacific Ocean
to find the stream where it had been born.
It had grown big in the ocean, and strong,
and it shone like silver.

All summer Simon had been waiting to catch
just such a fish, and here was one right in front of him.
Yet he didn't feel happy.

He watched the big, handsome fish pushing its nose
against the gravelly sides of the clam hole,
trying to find a way out, and he felt sorry for it.
He knew it would die if it didn't have enough water
to swim in. If only it could get back
to the sea, it would live.

Simon wanted the salmon to be safe in the sea,
where it could swim and leap and dive.
And where it would one day find its own stream.
He didn't know how he was going to save the salmon.
But he had to find a way.

"I won't let you die, Sukai," said Simon.
(*Sukai* was an old Indian name for the salmon
and it meant "king of the fishes.")

Simon thought of carrying the fish to the sea,
but he knew it was too big and heavy
and too slippery for him to pick up.
He thought about waiting for the tide to come in,
but he knew the salmon couldn't wait that long.
He looked up at the watching seagulls,
but all they said was *keer, keer*.
He must find a way.

Looking around, he saw his clam shovel,
and an idea popped into Simon's head.
He would dig a channel for the salmon to swim
down to the sea. That was all he had to do.
He began to dig and the wet sand was heavy,
but he would do it! He dug and dug.

After a while he stopped and looked to see
how far he had gone, and he had not gone very far at all.
He kept on digging. His mother called him for supper,
but he couldn't go because he hadn't finished yet.
The salmon was lying quietly now
in the shallow water, waiting.

The sun dipped low in the sky and the air became cool.
Simon's hands were red and he was getting a blister,
but he kept on digging.

At last, just when he thought he couldn't lift
another shovelful of sand, he looked up and there he was,
at the pool. The channel was finished.

Cold sea water flowed into it. When the salmon felt
the freshness of the sea, it began to move again.
Its nose found the opening to the channel and slowly,
slowly, the salmon began to swim down it.
Down to the sea.

Simon watched his shining salmon. Down, down,
down the channel it swam. At last it reached the sea.
It dived deep into the cool, green water, and then,
gleaming in the last rays of the setting sun,
it gave a great leap into the air.

And it seemed to Simon that the salmon flicked its tail
as if to say "thank you" before it disappeared
beneath the waves. "Good-bye, Sukai," called Simon.
The salmon was free at last. Soon it would be
in the deep, secret places of the sea.

Now the sun had set and a chilly wind was starting to blow.
Simon's hands were sore and his feet were cold,
but he felt warm inside. And happy.
He picked up his fishing pole and his shovel
and started for home.

And he knew, as he got near his house,
that it would be bright and cheery inside,
because lamplight shone golden through the windows.
And he knew that it would be nice and warm,
because he could see smoke curling out of the chimney.
And he knew that something good was cooking for supper,
because he could smell a delicious smell.

And Simon thought, as he opened the door,
that maybe he would go fishing again tomorrow, after all.
But not for a salmon.

Who blew out the candle?

Nate the Great Goes Undercover

by
Marjorie Weinman Sharmat

Chapter One

I, Nate the Great, am a detective.
I work hard, I rest hard. Tonight I am resting hard
from my last case. It was my first night case.

It started in the morning before breakfast.
I was walking my dog, Sludge. Sludge is my new dog.
I found him in a field eating a stale pancake.
I love pancakes. I knew he was my kind of dog.

I saw Oliver come out of his house. Oliver lives next door.
Sludge and I walked faster. Oliver walked faster.
Oliver caught up with us. He always catches up
with us. Oliver is a pest.

"There is a garbage snatcher in the neighbourhood,"
Oliver said. "Our can is tipped over
every night. I need help."

Oliver knows I am a detective. He knows I am
a good detective. "I will help you," I said.
"I, Nate the Great, will help you pick up your garbage."

"That is not the kind of help I need," Oliver said.
"I want to know who is taking the garbage every night."

"That is easy," I said. "Somebody hungry is taking
your garbage. Somebody very hungry. And sleepy.
Somebody sleepy from getting up every night
to take your garbage."

"Do you know anybody hungry and sleepy?" Oliver asked.

"Yes," I said. "Me. I will find the garbage snatcher
after I eat breakfast."

Sludge and I went home. I cooked a giant pancake.
I gave some to Sludge. Then we went outside.
I said to Sludge, "I'll ask questions while you sniff.
If you sniff any garbage smells, let me know."

I saw Rosamond coming down the street with her cats.
Rosamond did not look hungry or sleepy.
She looked like she always looks. Strange.
Sludge sniffed while I spoke.
"Rosamond, do you eat garbage?"

Rosamond said, "There are two thousand other things
I would eat before I would eat garbage. First,
I would eat hamburger, ice cream, candy, pickles,
bananas, potato chips, Krispy Krappies, relish,
doughnuts, spaghetti, ice cubes, mint leaves. . . ."

Rosamond kept talking. I did not have time to hear her list
of two thousand things. I walked on. Rosamond was still talking.

"Pretzels, artichokes, baked beans,
chocolate pudding, vegetable soup, walnuts...."

Rosamond had two thousand reasons for not taking
Oliver's garbage. But what about her cats?
I went back to Rosamond.

"Cauliflower, wafers, lamb chops," she said.
"Peanuts, egg salad...."

"Excuse me," I said. "Do your cats eat garbage?"

"No," Rosamond said. "My cats eat cat food, cheese,
tuna fish, milk, salmon pie, liver loaf...."

I walked away. I decided to look for Esmeralda.
Esmeralda always has her mouth open. She is either hungry
or about to yawn. I saw her sitting in front of her house.
Sludge sniffed. I spoke. "Do you get up at night
to visit Oliver's garbage can?" I asked.

"I would never visit anything that belongs
to Oliver," Esmeralda said.
"He might follow me."

Now I know why Esmeralda keeps
her mouth open. She has wise things to say.
She had given me an important clue.
No person would go near Oliver
or his garbage. Oliver is too much
of a pest.

Sludge and I went home. Oliver came over.
Oliver always comes over. Sludge sniffed Oliver.
I gave Sludge a pancake.

"Is the case solved?" Oliver asked.

"Part of it," I said.

"Which part?" he asked.

"I, Nate the Great, have found out who did not take your garbage. A person did not take your garbage."

"Well, who took it?" Oliver asked.

"That is the part that is not solved," I said.
"I, Nate the Great, say that an animal or bird took it.
An animal or bird that goes out in the night.
I will find out what and I will be back."

Sometimes I, Nate the Great, need help. I went
to the library. I read about birds that go out
in the night. They are called Strigiformes
and Caprimulgiformes. I wrote the names down.

Then I crossed them out. Birds with names like that would not eat anything called garbage. Then I read about cats, rats, bats, mice, shrews, skunks, raccoons, opossums, and moles. They all go out at night. I read about what they like and what they do not like.

Then I went home. Oliver came over. I said, "A cat, rat, bat, mouse, shrew, skunk, raccoon, opossum, or mole is taking your garbage."

"Which one?" Oliver asked.

"I don't know. But tonight, I, Nate the Great, will find out." I left a note for my mother.

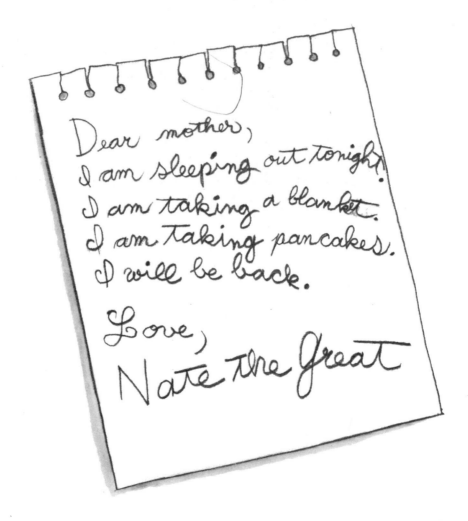

Dear mother,
I am sleeping out tonight.
I am taking a blanket.
I am taking pancakes.
I will be back.

Love,
Nate the Great

Chapter Two

I went out into the yard. It was cold out there.
I asked Sludge if I could share his doghouse.
I crawled in. Sludge crawled out. It was a small doghouse.
I looked out the window of the doghouse.
I could not see Oliver's garbage can.
I crawled out of the doghouse. I left Sludge a pancake.

Where could I hide? I, Nate the Great, knew where to hide.
In the garbage can. I was sorry I knew.

Detective work is not fun and games. Detective work
is dirty garbage cans instead of clean beds.
Detective work is banana peels, dishrags, milk cartons,
floor sweepings, cigar ashes, fleas, and me
all together in one can.

I peeked out from under the cover. The street was quiet.
Then I heard a sound. *Crunch! Crackle! Klunk!*
The sound was close to me. The sound was me.
The garbage can was crunchy and crackly and klunky.

Every time I moved, it was crunchier and cracklier.
I lifted up the cover. I got out. I had a new plan.
A better plan. I would not wait for the garbage snatcher.
I would go out and find him.

I crept down the street. I looked to the right
and to the left and behind me. Right, left, behind.
Right, left, behind. *Smack!* Something big hit me.

It was in front of me. The one place I forgot to look.
I do not think I made a dent in the telephone pole.
I kept creeping and looking. Right, left, behind, front.
Right, left, behind, front.

I came to a field. Animals like fields. I saw an animal.
I, Nate the Great, was in luck. I crept closer.
I, Nate the Great, was in bad luck. It was a skunk.
I started to walk backward. I saw some stuff
on the ground next to the skunk. It looked like garbage.
I walked forward to see. I saw some garbage.
The skunk saw me. The skunk stamped his feet.
He raised his tail. I, Nate the Great, did not run
fast enough. But the case was solved.
The skunk was the garbage snatcher.

I went home. I wrote a note to Oliver.
I put it in his mailbox.

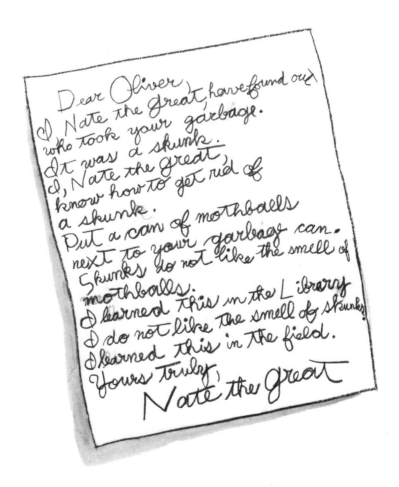

It was not morning yet. But I knew
there was something I must do right away.
I was glad the water was hot. In fact,
that is how I spent most of the next day.

The following morning Oliver came over.
"The case is unsolved," he said.
"The garbage can is tipped again."

"Impossible," I said.

"Come and see my garbage," Oliver said.

I, Nate the Great, have had better invitations.
But I went.

The can was tipped, all right.

"And here is the can of mothballs," Oliver said.
"So who is the garbage snatcher?" he asked.

"I, Nate the Great, will find out,
no matter how long or how many baths it takes."
I walked away. Sludge followed me. He was doing
a lot of sniffing. But I, Nate the Great,
had a lot of thinking to do.

I gave Sludge a pancake. There must be a clue I missed.
Sludge ignored the pancake. He was thinking, too.
I thought harder. And harder. Then I knew what the clue was.
All I needed was the proof.

I left a note for my mother.

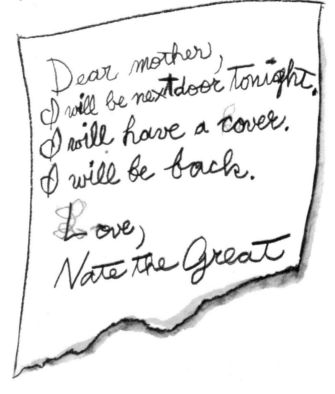

Dear mother,
I will be nextdoor Tonight.
I will have a cover.
I will be back.

Love,
Nate the Great

I went to the garbage can. I stepped inside.
I put the cover over me. I left a space to look out
and to breathe. I knew that was important.
I waited. Nothing happened.

Something came up to the can. Something knocked the cover to the ground. Something looked inside.
"Something" was Sludge.

Sludge was surprised to see me. But I,
Nate the Great, had been expecting to see Sludge.
I knew that Sludge was the garbage snatcher.
And I knew why. Sludge was tired of my pancakes.
How could anybody be tired of pancakes? Sludge was looking for his own snack. Sludge was hungry.

I took him back to his doghouse. I gave him a bone
and a bowl of dog food. Someday Sludge will be
a great detective, when he learns to sniff more
and snatch less.

I wanted to take a bath. But I was too tired.
I wanted to write a note to Oliver.
But I was too tired. Tomorrow Oliver will come over.
Oliver always comes over.

Now I am resting. I can hear the sounds of the night.
I can hear the sounds of a crunchy bone
being crunched. They are good sounds.

My first night case is over.
Maybe it will be my last night case.
I, Nate the Great, am pooped.

Rattlesnake Skipping Song

by
Dennis Lee

Mississauga rattlesnakes
Eat brown bread.
Mississauga rattlesnakes
Fall down dead.
If you catch a caterpillar
Feed him apple juice;
But if you catch a rattlesnake
Turn him loose!

Molly Whuppie Fights the Giant

retold by
David Booth

Once upon a time, there was an old woodcutter
who had many children. He worked as hard as he could,
but he couldn't feed them all.
He took the three youngest children,
gave them each a slice of bread and treacle,
and left them alone in the forest.

The children ate the bread and treacle,
and walked and walked and walked
until they were completely lost in the forest.
Just as it was beginning to get dark, they spied
a small and beaming light between the trees.

The three children followed the light to a cottage.
Molly Whuppie, the youngest and cleverest of them all,
knocked at the door. A woman came to the door
and asked them what they wanted.
Molly Whuppie said, "Something to eat."

"Eat?" said the woman, "Eat! Why my husband's a giant,
and he would eat you!"

But they were tired and hungry, and Molly begged
the woman to let them in.

At last, the woman took them in,
sat them down by the fire, and gave them some bread
and milk. Before they had taken one sip, or one bite,
there came a thumping at the door. (No mistaking that.)

It was the giant arriving home, and in he came.
"Ha!" he said, squinting at the children,
"What have we here?"

His wife said, "Three poor, cold, hungry, lost,
little children. You eat your supper, my husband,
and leave the children to me."

The giant said nothing, sat down, and ate his supper.
Between bites, he looked at the children.

Now, the giant had three daughters of his own.
His wife put all six of them into the same bed.
She thought that this would keep the strangers safe.
But before he went to bed, the giant hung
three chains of gold around his daughters' necks.
Then the giant hung three chains of golden straw
around the three strangers' necks.

Soon, the other five children were asleep in the giant bed,
but Molly lay awake, listening. She rose up softly,
and changed over, one by one, the necklaces
of gold and of straw. Now it was that Molly and her sisters
wore the chains of gold, and the giant's three daughters,
the chains of straw. Then, Molly lay down again.

In the middle of the night, the giant tiptoed
into the room. Carefully, with fingers and thumb,
he plucked up the three children with the straw necklaces,
carried them downstairs, and bolted them up in his cellar.
"So, so, my pretty chickabiddies, now you're safe."
And he bolted the door.

As soon as all was quiet again,
Molly Whuppie thought it was high time
she and her sisters were out of that house.
So she woke them up, whispering in their ears,
and they slipped down the stairs and out into the forest.
They never stopped running until morning.

At day break, they came to another house.
It stood beside a pool of water, full of wild swans.

It was the house of the King.
So Molly went in and told her story to the King.
The King listened, and when it was finished, said:
"Well, Molly, that's one thing done and done well.
But there is another thing that you could do
and that would be better."

The King knew the giant of old, and he told Molly to go back
and steal for him the giant's sword that hung beside his bed.
If she did, the King said he would give her eldest sister
his eldest son for a husband, and then Molly's sister
would be a princess. Molly looked at the eldest prince,
and smiled and said she would try.

That very evening she muffled herself up, and made her way
back through the forest to the house of the giant.
First she listened at the window, and there she heard
the giant eating his supper. She crept into the house
and hid under his bed. In the middle of the night,
Molly climbed softly up to the great bed and unhooked
the giant's sword. The sword hung from a nail on the wall.
The shutters shook with the snores of the giant.

When Molly came to the door, she accidentally rattled
the sword and woke up the giant. Then Molly ran
and the giant ran and they both ran, and at last they came
to the Bridge of One Hair. Molly ran over,
but not the giant, for run over he couldn't.
Instead, he shook his fist at her across the bridge,
and shouted: "Woe betide you, Molly Whuppie,
if you ever come back again."

But Molly laughed and said: "Maybe twice I'll come
to see you, and maybe once again."
Then Molly carried off the sword to the King.
And soon, her eldest sister married the King's eldest son.

After the wedding, the King said: "That was a thing
done well, Molly. But I know another,
and that's better still. Steal the purse that lies
under the giant's pillow, and I'll marry your second sister
to my second son." Molly looked at the King's second son,
and said she would try.

So, she muffled herself up and stole through the forest
to the giant's house. There he was, guzzling his supper
as usual. This time, Molly hid herself in the closet.
(A stuffy place that was.)

In the middle of the night, Molly heard the giant snoring.
She crept out of the closet, took a deep breath,
and slid her fingers under his pillow.
Suddenly, the giant called out in his sleep.

His wife said, "Lie easy, man!
It's those bones you had for supper."

Then Molly pushed in her fingers a bit further.
She felt the purse. But as she pulled the purse
from under the pillow, a gold coin dropped out of it
and clanked onto the floor.

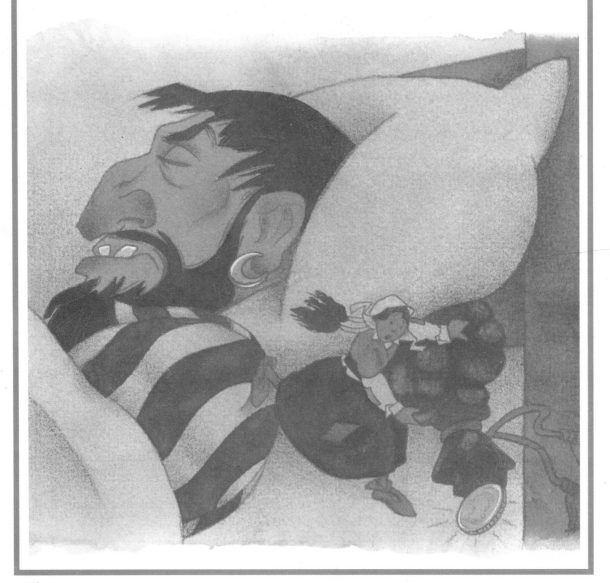

At the sound of it, the giant woke.
Then Molly ran and the giant ran, and they both ran.
They ran and ran until they came to the Bridge of One Hair.

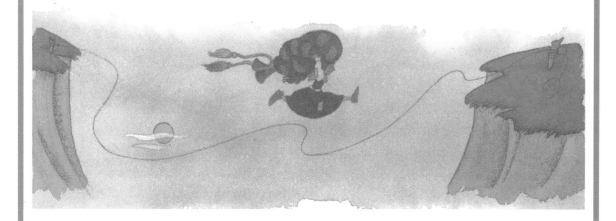

Molly got over, but the giant stayed, for get over
he couldn't. Then he cried out: "Woe betide you,
Molly Whuppie, if you ever come back again."

But Molly only laughed and called back to him:
"Maybe thrice I'll come to see you,
and maybe once again."
So she took the purse to the King,
and her second sister married his second son.

When the wedding was over, the King said
to Molly, "That was yet a better thing done
and done for good. But I know a better thing yet,
and that's the best of all.
Steal the giant's ring off his thumb,
and you shall marry my youngest son.
And truly, Molly, you always were my favourite."
Molly looked at the King's youngest son,
laughed, and said she would try.

This time, she stole into the giant's house and hid
in the chimney corner. In the dead of night,
when the giant was snoring, she crept towards his bed.
By good chance, the giant lay on his back,
with his arm hanging down.

It was the arm that had the hand at the end of it
on which was the great thumb that wore the ring.
First she tugged softly at the ring. Little by little
it slid down, and over the knuckle bone.
But just as Molly had slipped it off,
the giant woke with a roar. He gripped her
and lifted her clean up into the dark over his head.

"Ah-ha! Molly Whuppie," said he. "Once too many is never again.
If I'd done the ill to you as you have done to me,
what would I be getting for my pains?"

"Why," Molly answered, "I would bundle you up
into a sack, put the cat and dog inside with you,
and a needle and thread and a great pair of shears,
and I'd hang you up on the wall, be off to the wood,
cut down the thickest stick I could get,
come home, take you down, and beat you to a jelly.
That's what I'd do!"

"And that, Molly," said the giant, chuckling to himself
with pleasure, "that's just what I will be doing with you."

So he rose up out of bed, fetched a sack,
put Molly into the sack, put the cat and the dog
in the sack, put a needle and thread
and a stout pair of shears in the sack,
and hung her up on the wall. Then he went
into the forest to cut a big stick.

When he was gone, Molly stroked the dog
with one hand and the cat with the other.
Then she sang with a high, clear voice,
"Oh, if only everybody could see what I can see!"

The giant's wife said, "What do you see?"

But Molly only laughed and said, "Oh, if only everybody
could see what I can see!"

The giant's wife begged Molly to take her up
into the sack so that she could see what Molly saw.
Then Molly took the shears and cut a hole in the sack,
jumped out of the sack, helped the giant's wife into it,
and sewed up the hole with the needle and thread
as fast as she could.

But it was pitch black in the sack.
The giant's wife saw nothing, and soon asked
to be let out again. Molly never answered her,
but hid at the back of the door. Home at last
came the giant, with a quickwood stick in his hand.
And he began to strike the sack with the stick.

His wife cried, "Stay, man! It's me, man! Oh, man,
it's me, man!"

But the dog barked and the cat squeaked,
and he didn't hear her voice.

Then Molly crept softly out from behind
the door, but the giant saw her. He gave a roar!
And Molly ran and the giant ran,
and they both ran, until they came to
the Bridge of One Hair. And Molly slipped
over it, but the giant couldn't. And he cried out
in a dreadful voice: "Woe betide you,
Molly Whuppie, if you ever come back again!"

But Molly waved her hand at the giant and said:
"Never again, I'll come to see you.
Four times is enough for all."

Then Molly ran off with the ring in her pocket.
She married the King's youngest son.
There was a feast that was a finer feast than all feasts
that had ever been in the King's house before.
Although there were guests by the hundreds
from all parts of the country, the giant never so much
as gnawed a bone!

The Ox-Cart Man
by
Donald Hall

In October he backed his ox into his cart
and he and his family filled it up
with everything they made or grew all year long
that was left over.

He packed a bag of wool
he sheared from the sheep in April.

He packed a shawl his wife wove on a loom
from yarn spun at the spinning wheel
from sheep sheared in April.

He packed five pairs of mittens
his daughter knit
from yarn spun at the spinning wheel
from sheep sheared in April.

He packed candles the family made.
He packed linen made from flax they grew.
He packed shingles he split himself.
He packed birch brooms his son carved
with a borrowed kitchen knife.

He packed potatoes they dug from their garden—
but first he counted out potatoes enough to eat all winter
and potatoes for seed next spring.
He packed a barrel of apples
honey and honeycombs
turnips and cabbages

a wooden box of maple sugar
from the maples they tapped in March
when they boiled and boiled and boiled the sap away.
He packed a bag of goose feathers that his children collected
from the barnyard geese.

When his cart was full, he waved good-bye to his wife,
his daughter, and his son
and he walked at his ox's head ten days

over hills, through valleys, by streams
past farms and villages
until he came to Portsmouth
and Portsmouth Market.

He sold the bag of wool.

He sold the shawl his wife made.

He sold five pairs of mittens.

He sold candles and shingles.

He sold birch brooms.

He sold potatoes.

He sold apples.

He sold honey and honeycombs,
turnips and cabbages.

He sold maple sugar.

He sold a bag of goose feathers.

Then he sold the wooden box he carried the maple sugar in.

Then he sold the barrel he carried the apples in.

Then he sold the bag he carried the potatoes in.

Then he sold his ox cart.

Then he sold his ox, and kissed him good-bye on his nose.

Then he sold his ox's yoke and harness.

With his pockets full of coins,
he walked through Portsmouth Market.
He bought an iron kettle to hang over the fire at home,
and for his daughter he bought an embroidery needle
that came from a boat in the harbour
that had sailed all the way from England,
and for his son he bought a Barlow knife,
for carving birch brooms with
and for the whole family he bought
two pounds of wintergreen peppermint candies.

Then he walked home, with the needle and the knife

and the wintergreen peppermint candies

tucked into the kettle,

and a stick over his shoulder,

stuck through the kettle's handle,

and coins still in his pockets,

past farms and villages,

over hills, through valleys, by streams,

until he came to his farm,

and his son, his daughter,

and his wife were waiting for him,

and his daughter took her needle and began stitching,

and his son took his Barlow knife and started whittling,

and they cooked dinner in their new kettle,

and afterward everyone ate a wintergreen peppermint candy,

and that night the ox-cart man sat in front of his fire

stitching new harness for the young ox in the barn

and he carved a new yoke and split shingles all winter,

and sawed planks for a new cart

while his wife made flax into linen all winter,

and his daughter embroidered linen all winter,

and his son carved Indian brooms from birch all winter,

and everybody made candles,

and in March they tapped the sugar maple trees
and boiled the sap down,

and in April they sheared the sheep,
spun yarn
and wove and knitted,

and in May they planted potatoes, turnips, and cabbages,
while apple blossoms bloomed and fell,
while bees woke up, starting to make new honey,
and geese squawked in the barnyard,
dropping feathers as soft as clouds.

There's a Party at Mona's Tonight

by
Harry Allard

Potter Pig was peacefully nightfishing
for guppies when a cart clattered by overhead.

"There's a party at Mona's tonight!" someone shouted.

Potter Pig pricked up his ears. "A party at Mona's,"
he said. "Hmmm." Putting his fishing pole aside,
Potter rowed to shore.

He raced to Mona's on his motorcycle.
"It's odd that Mona didn't invite me," he said.
"Mona always invites me to her lovely parties.
The mailman must have lost the invitation."

At Mona's, Potter heard laughter, music, and dancing.
And he smelled delicious food. He knocked on Mona's door.
"Open up, Mona!" he shouted. "It's me, Potter Pig."

Mona stomped to the door and yelled, "Go away,
Potter Pig!" With that, she slammed the door
in his face.

Potter sat down on the front step.
"Mona must have mistaken me for some other Potter Pig,"
he said. He knocked on the door again.

This time Mona stuck her head out the window and yelled,
"Beat it, Potter!" Then she yanked down the shade.

"Strange," said Potter.

Potter went home and poured himself a cup of cocoa.
"I just don't understand it," he sighed.
"Doesn't Mona realize I'm always the life of the party?"
Potter was just not going to take no for an answer.
By hook or by crook, he was going to attend Mona's lovely party.

Later that evening, a statue was delivered to Mona's.
Mona was thrilled. But when the statue sneezed,
Mona booted it out the door.

"Rats!" said Potter Pig, heading home.
"I'll just have to think of some other way."

Fifteen minutes later, a Scottish bagpiper appeared at the party.
"You can't fool me, Potter Pig!" yelled Mona,
and out he went, bagpipes and all.

Potter decided to tunnel his way into Mona's basement.
He said he was from the gas company and had come
to read the gas meter. Mona didn't buy it.
"Scram, Potter!" she said.

Potter put on his thinking cap.
"I will not give up," he said, clenching his fists.
"Where there's a will, there's a way!"

Potter hired a dirigible and had himself lowered down
Mona's chimney disguised as Santa Claus.
But, since it was the middle of summer,
Potter could not bamboozle Mona.
She showed him the door.

A little while later, Potter ran into Blossom Skunk.
"I think Mona is mad at me," he said.
"But I just don't know why."

"Why don't you ask her?" suggested Blossom.

Potter dialed Mona's number. "Mona," he said,
"why are you mad at me?"

"Because you told Bruce the Toad I had big feet!" said Mona.

"Why, Mona, I never said you had big feet," said Potter.

"Well in that case," said Mona, "why don't you come
to my party?"

Mona greeted Potter with open arms. "We've missed you!"
she said, giving him a party hat. Potter was so glad
that he had made up with Mona. Soon, he was having
the time of his life.

But while Mona was dancing a wild fandango,
Potter turned to Bruce the Toad and whispered,
"But you know, Mona does have big feet!"

"I heard that, Potter!" cried Mona.
And she kicked Potter out. "And don't you dare
come back!" she shouted.

Later that evening, a lady knocked at the door.
"I'm your Aunt Gertrude, Mona," she said.
Don't you recognize me, dear?"

Hallowe'en Poetry

I'm Skeleton

I'm the local Skeleton
who walks this
street.
This is my beat.
Beware!
I'm not very hairy
but I scare
everyone I meet.

People quiver
when they see me.
They flee me!
They shiver
if they must walk
alone.

Oops, there's a dog.
I must run.
His tail has a wag.
He wants to play tag.
And how he would like a
bone!

Witch Goes Shopping

Witch rides off
Upon her broom
Finds a space
To park it.
Takes a shiny shopping cart
Into the supermarket.
Smacks her lips and reads
The list of things she needs:

"Six bats' wings
Worms in brine
Ears of toads
Eight or nine.
Slugs and bugs
Snake skins dried
Buzzard innards
Pickled, fried."

Witch takes herself
From shelf to shelf
Cackling all the while.
Up and down and up and down and
In and out each aisle.
Out come cans and cartons
Tumbling to the floor.
"This," says Witch, now all a-twitch,
"Is a crazy store.
I can't find a single thing
I am looking for!"

No One

In this room
there's not a
breeze.

No one sneezed
the littlest
sneeze.

No one wheezed
the faintest
wheeze.

The door's shut tight
with a big brass
handle.

Who?
Who
blew out the candle?

Dear Country Witch

Dear Country Witch,

Come try out
city Halloween.
It's
keener
meaner
Halloweener!

What if yours
is greener?
We'll climb
through smoke and
dust and
grime
upon my
vacuum cleaner.

    City Witch

Bedtime Stories

"Tell me a story,"
Says Witch's Child.

"About the Beast
So fierce and wild.

About a Ghost
That shrieks and groans.

A Skeleton
That rattles bones.

About a Monster
Crawly-creepy.

Something nice
To make me sleepy."

by
Lilian Moore

Old Devil Wind
by
Bill Martin Jr.

One dark and stormy night
Ghost floated out of the wall
and he began to *wail*.

Stool said,
"Ghost, Ghost, why do you wail?"

Ghost said,
"It's a dark and stormy night
and so I wail."

And Stool said,
"Then I shall thump."
So Stool began to *thump*!

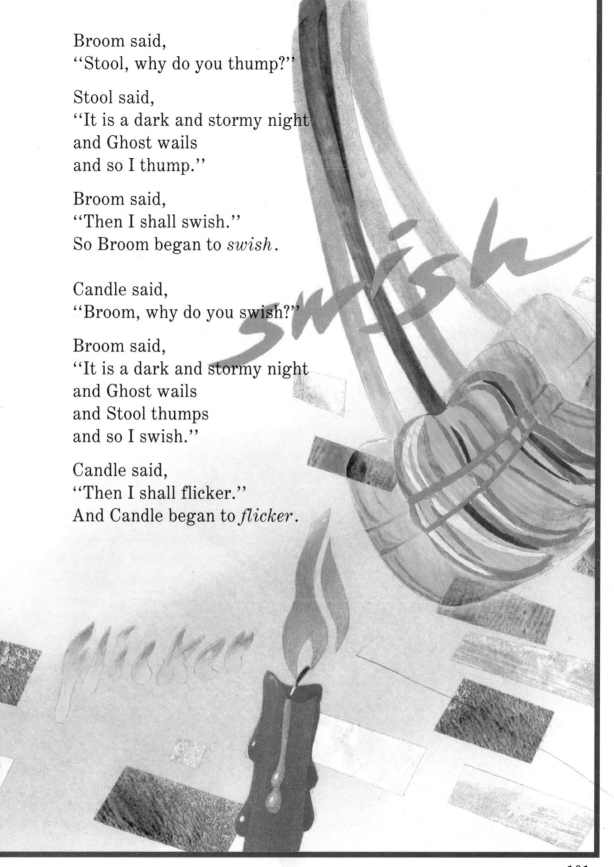

Broom said,
"Stool, why do you thump?"

Stool said,
"It is a dark and stormy night
and Ghost wails
and so I thump."

Broom said,
"Then I shall swish."
So Broom began to *swish*.

Candle said,
"Broom, why do you swish?"

Broom said,
"It is a dark and stormy night
and Ghost wails
and Stool thumps
and so I swish."

Candle said,
"Then I shall flicker."
And Candle began to *flicker*.

Fire said,
"Candle, why do you flicker?"

Candle said,
"It is a dark and stormy night
and Ghost wails
and Stool thumps
and Broom swishes
and so I flicker."

Fire said,
"Then I shall smoke."
And Fire began to *smoke*.

Window said,
"Fire, why do you smoke?"

Fire said,
"It is a dark and stormy night
and Ghost wails
and Stool thumps
and Broom swishes
and Candle flickers
and so I smoke."

Window said,
"Then I shall rattle."
And Window began to *rattle*.

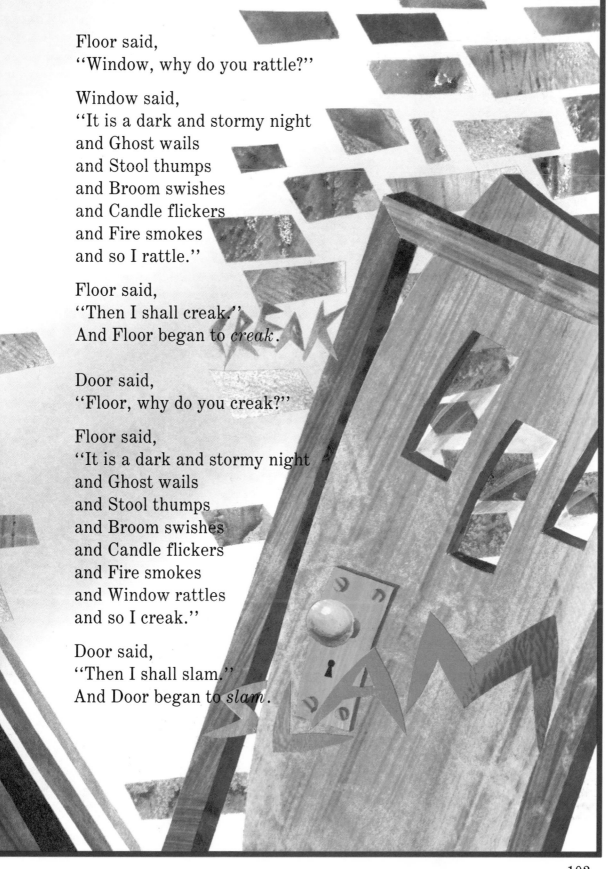

Floor said,
"Window, why do you rattle?"

Window said,
"It is a dark and stormy night
and Ghost wails
and Stool thumps
and Broom swishes
and Candle flickers
and Fire smokes
and so I rattle."

Floor said,
"Then I shall creak."
And Floor began to *creak*.

Door said,
"Floor, why do you creak?"

Floor said,
"It is a dark and stormy night
and Ghost wails
and Stool thumps
and Broom swishes
and Candle flickers
and Fire smokes
and Window rattles
and so I creak."

Door said,
"Then I shall slam."
And Door began to *slam*.

Owl said,
"Door, why do you slam?"

Door said,
"It is a dark and stormy night
and Ghost wails
and Stool thumps
and Broom swishes
and Candle flickers
and Fire smokes
and Window rattles
and Floor creaks
and so I slam."

Owl said,
"Then I shall hoot."
And Owl began to *hoot*.

Witch said,
"Owl, why do you hoot?"

Owl said,
"It is a dark and stormy night
and Ghost wails
and Stool thumps
and Broom swishes
and Candle flickers
and Fire smokes
and Window rattles
and Floor creaks
and Door slams
and so I hoot."

Witch said,
"Then I shall fly around the house."

Wind said,
"Witch, why do you fly
around the house?"

Witch said,
"It is a dark and stormy night
and Ghost wails
and Stool thumps
and Broom swishes
and Candle flickers
and Fire smokes
and Window rattles
and Floor creaks
and Door slams
and Owl hoots
and so I fly
around the house."

Wind said,
"Then I shall blow."
And Wind began to *blow*.

And he blew away the ghost
and the house
and the broom
and the stool
and the candle
and the fire
and the window
and the floor
and the door
and the owl
and the witch.

And they didn't come back
'til Halloween night.

Yummers
by
James Marshall

Emily Pig was upset.
She was gaining weight and she didn't know why.
"Maybe I should get more exercise," she said to herself.

The next day Emily jumped rope.
"I don't really like this," she said, huffing and puffing.

"I have a better idea," said her best friend, Eugene.
"Why don't you come for a nice long stroll with me?
Walking is the best exercise of all."

Emily was delighted. "Walking is more fun," she said.
"It doesn't seem like exercise."

"And there are so many lovely things to see," said Eugene.

But walking made Emily hungry.
"Do you think we have time for a little snack?" she asked.

Eugene knew where to get the most delicious sandwiches.
"Oh, yummers," said Emily, "all my favourites.
But which one should I choose?"

"Have more than one," said Eugene.

"I don't want to make a pig of myself," said Emily.
"I'll just have a tuna fish and a jelly delight."

"That sounds sensible," said Eugene.

But the sandwiches only made Emily hungrier.
"Oh, yummers!" she squealed
when she saw the corn-on-the-cob stand.
And what pig can resist corn on the cob?

The corn was especially tasty,
but very soon Emily's nose began to twitch.
"What is that wonderful smell?" she asked.

"It's coming from Granner's Tea Room," said Eugene.

"Granner would never forgive us if we didn't pop in
to say hello," said Emily.

Granner's Tea Room was cozy indeed.
"The scones were scrumptious. Another platter of scones,
please," Emily called. "And lots of hot butter and jam."

Eugene was still nibbling on his first scone.

"I'm afraid you didn't get enough to eat, Eugene,"
said Emily.

"Yes, I did," answered Eugene.
"My scone was very good."

But Emily was not satisfied.

"Oh, look!" she squealed. "Eskimo pies!"
Eugene didn't particularly like eskimo pies.
But Emily did. She ate three in a row.

As a special treat Eugene purchased a box
of Girl Scout cookies.

"Yummers," said Emily. But everybody knows
that Girl Scout cookies are even better with milk.

"Let's have a glass of milk with our cookies
at the drugstore," said Emily.

"Nice idea," said Eugene.

But inside the drugstore Emily couldn't help ordering
a vanilla malt, a banana split, and a small dish
of peach ice cream. "This is simply yummers," she said.
Eugene sipped a glass of skimmed milk.

Leaving the drugstore, Eugene snapped his fingers.
"I almost forgot. This morning I drank
the last of my jasmine tea. Do you mind stopping
at the supermarket?"

"Certainly not," replied Emily.
While Eugene was waiting in line, Emily discovered
the free pizza. "It's so important to sample
new products," she said.

In the park, Emily felt awful. "I have a tummy ache,"
she moaned. She could barely finish her cherry pop
and candied apple. Eugene took Emily home in a taxi.
He was very concerned.

The next morning Eugene paid a call on his sick friend.
But Emily was feeling much better.
"What do you suppose was the matter?" asked Eugene.

"It must have been all that walking," replied his friend.

Eugene smiled. "Maybe you should stay in bed
and eat plenty of food."

"Oh, yummers," said Emily.

The Sandwich
by
Ian Wallace and Angela Wood

"My name is Vincenzo Ferrante
and I am in Grade 3 at Clinton Street Public School.
I live at 538 Manning Avenue in a flat
over Milgrom's Variety with my father, my sister Lisa,
my Nonna, Zio Salvatore; and my two rabbits, Tucci and Zeppo.
They live in a wire and wood cage that Papa and I made for them.

"Mamma used to live with us, but she died a year ago
which makes me sad sometimes. When I'm unhappy
I climb into my father's lap and feel much better.

"After Mamma's death, Nonna came over from Italy and has been helping Papa to care for Lisa and me. Every Sunday she takes us to see him at work, driving his streetcar up and down St. Clair Avenue. She helps me make my bed, cooks our favourite things to eat, and tells us bedtime stories in Italian because Nonna can't speak English.

"Until today I have always eaten lunch at home. Tomorrow for the first time I am going to eat at school. Mamma and Nonna would say, 'Vincenzo, you can get a better lunch at home than out of a bag. So, you'll eat at home.'

"Nonna is sick and was taken to the Toronto General Hospital so she can get better. Mrs. Leone next door is going to take care of Lisa until Papa gets home from work. Zio Zalvatore will take care of himself. He sleeps all day and works all night at the ice cream factory."

"Papa, can I butter the bread?" asked Vincenzo, climbing into his chair at the kitchen table.

"If you want, Vincenzo. That would be a big help. Here's a knife and the butter is on the counter beside the toaster."

Returning to the table he watched intently as his father held the bread with one hand and cut thick slices with skill and ease.

"This is very good bread, Vincenzo, fresh out of Fiore's oven. It's the best bread in Toronto!"

"You always say that Fiore's is the best bread in Toronto, Papa."

"Well, it is good. Isn't it?"

"Yeah, but I haven't tasted any other!" said Vincenzo, spreading the knife across a slice of bread. "How's this?"

"Good. Very good."

"Now, what kind of sandwich do you want, provolone cheese, mortadella, meatballs or salami?"

"What are you going to have for lunch, Papa?"

"Hmmmm. Let's see. Meatballs are good, but the bread becomes soggy if it turns hot outside. Salami?...Uhn...Not tomorrow.

Mortadella and provolone. Such an aroma!
Here, Vincenzo, taste this.
Good, eh?...Now, that's what I'll have.''

"Me too, Papa. That's what I want.
Mortadella and provolone, just like you!''
Vincenzo placed the thin slices of mortadella
carefully on the bread as his father cut the provolone.

"There we are, Vincenzo. This slice goes on top
and we are done. Will you hand me the wax paper?
Now, if you hold this end down I'll fold
the other ends over.''

"Can we have some anisette cookies and a can
of orange juice with our lunch, Papa?''

"If that's what you want, then that's what we'll have.''

Together they filled their brown lunch bags;
first the mortadella and provolone sandwich
and then the anisette cookies, also wrapped in wax paper.
The can of orange juice was placed on its side
and the top of the bag folded down.

"It's getting late, Vincenzo, so off to bed you go.
Wash your face and hands and remember both sides.
Brush your teeth, go to the bathroom and I will be in
to say goodnight."

"Okay, Papa. But will you tell me a story
about when you were a little boy?"

"If you promise to go right to sleep.
And remember, just one."

His lunch bag in one hand and school books in the other,
Vincenzo raced down the two flights of stairs
to the street below. The sun was shining on his face
and he felt good inside. "Today," he said
to a passing squirrel, "I am going to eat
in the cafeteria and are we going to have fun!"

The clock ticked and ticked and ticked,
but the morning seemed like it would never end.
Watching its measured movements made Vincenzo's eyes blurr.
His stomach began to groan and toss, signalling eleven-thirty.

"Vincenzo!" shouted Matt. "Come'n eat with us!"

"Okay," he replied, running towards his friend.
Matt threw an arm around Vincenzo's shoulder
and like a two-headed monster they strutted down the hall.
Hans, Cindy, Rita, and Paul were waiting at the table
by the window. Vincenzo dropped his lunch on the table
and sat on the end of the bench beside Rita.

"Vincenzo," she asked, "how's your Nonna today?"

"She's still sick. Papa took her to the hospital yesterday. That's why I am eating here instead of at home."

"She'll get better," assured Rita. "Don't worry. At least you get to eat lunch with us!"

Vincenzo turned and glanced around the table at the lunches which were now coming out of their bags.

"They're all the same except mine," he whispered to himself.

"Peanut butter and jam is my favourite sandwich," stated Paul.

"Mine too," said Rita, holding hers in front of her face. "I won't eat any other sandwich and that makes my mother so mad. She says that someday I am going to turn into a peanut! That would be neat, eh?"

"Yeah. Rita the Peanut," giggled Cindy.
Everyone nodded, laughing.

"Peeeeeww!" shouted Matt, "What's that stink? I've never smelled anything like it at our table before."

"Dead socks!" screeched Rita, grabbing her nose.
Heads turned, sniffing back and forth, up and down.

"Vincenzo," sniffed Matt. "It's Vincenzo's sandwich!"
His friends covered their noses and began to laugh.
"Vincenzo eats stinky meat!" laughed Matt.

"Vincenzo eats stinky meat!" sang Rita, Hans, Paul, and Cindy.
"Vincenzo eats stinky meat!" rang throughout the cafeteria.

Vincenzo didn't sing or laugh. He dropped his head
onto his chest and wiped away the stinging in his eyes.
The sandwich was staring him in the face.
With one quick movement, he grabbed it
and shoved it into the bag.
"The garbage," he thought, "that's where it belongs
and then I can run out of the cafeteria!"

But he didn't run outside. His friends,
finishing their lunch, went into the schoolyard
to play tag. They'd asked him to come along,
but he didn't want to go. Instead, he sat alone
for the remainder of the lunch hour.
He returned to the classroom
and quickly shoved the lunch into his desk.
"No one will see or smell it there," he thought.
The afternoon passed even more slowly than the morning.

When Vincenzo returned home that day his father noticed
that he was still carrying his lunch.
"Vincenzo," asked his father, "what did you eat for lunch?"

"Nothing."

"Nothing! You took a good lunch to school and ate nothing?
What's the matter, are you sick?"

"No Papa, I'm not sick. I didn't feel like eating,
that's all."

"The day that you don't eat your lunch, Vincenzo,
there *is* something wrong. Please, tell me what it is!"

Vincenzo shifted his weight from one foot to the other
and back again. His left hand moved across his face
and stopped behind his ear where it began to scratch.
"My friends...Umm...they...uh...laughed at my sandwich
and shouted, 'Vincenzo eats stinky meat!' "

"Ohhh," sighed his father. "So that's it. Come here."

Vincenzo climbed into his father's lap as he had done
many times before and waited for him to speak.
"Why do you think they laughed at you?"

"Because my sandwich stinks, that's why!
But it is a good sandwich, isn't it?"

"Do you like mortadella and provolone, Vincenzo?"

"Yes, Papa, I do."

"Then it is a good sandwich. Your friends laughed
because it was different. It smelled strange,
looked different, and it was new to them."

"Are you sure?" asked Vincenzo, doubtfully.

"Yes, son, I'm sure. Tomorrow when you go to school
and your friends laugh at your sandwich,
you laugh with them. Then they won't laugh any more."
He paused, "That is, if you want to take
another mortadella and provolone sandwich to school.
Or would you like me to buy you some peanut butter and jam?"

Vincenzo sat still and thoughtful in his father's arms
and then answered, "No Papa, you don't have to buy me
peanut butter and jam. I'll take my own sandwich."

"Good, Vincenzo. Always remember, you are who you are
and you have nothing to be ashamed of.
Now, will you help me get supper ready?"

"Sure!"

Late that night, he dreamed. He was seated
at a table twelve feet high in the middle of a large room
while bears danced around the walls.
There, set in front of him, was the biggest
and most beautiful jar of peanut butter and jam
that he had ever seen. With a large gold knife,
he dug into the glass jar and spread
a huge brown and red glob across a slice of bread.
He smiled down with delight at his family who looked
very sad and kept eating and eating and eating.

"Vincenzo, why are you taking so long?"

"I'll be there in a minute, Matt. You go ahead."

"Hurry up, then. We have to eat fast so we can play
outside longer," shouted Matt, racing off down the hall.
When Vincenzo reached the cafeteria table,
his friends were seated as they had been the day before.
"Vincenzo," asked Matt, "what did you bring
for lunch today? Something stinkless I hope."
Everyone laughed, except Vincenzo.

"No," he replied firmly, "I have stinky meat and cheese."

"Oh no. Vincenzo eats stinky meat again," groaned Rita,
grabbing her nose, "and I have to sit beside him!"
Matt laughed, and Rita laughed, as did Hans, Cindy,
and Paul. But louder than them all laughed Vincenzo.

"I eat stinky meat!" he shouted at the top of his lungs.
Startled, his friends looked towards him.

"I dare you to eat some peanut butter and jam!" blurted Cindy.

"I dare you!" threatened Matt. "I dare you!"

"I don't want your peanut butter and jam.
I have my own sandwich that my Papa and I made."
Vincenzo glanced around the table and met five pairs of eyes
staring into his. He felt sweaty all over and wondered
if it showed on his face. "No," he thought, "I won't take
a dare," and took a big bite into his sandwich
and another bite and another.

His friends sat and watched in amazement.
Vincenzo was eating a stinky meat sandwich
and seemed to like it! Everyone began to eat
except Matt who stared intently
at the other half of Vincenzo's sandwich.
Slowly, his arm crept across the table
and, picking the sandwich up with one hand,
lifted it to his mouth.

There it sat for a few moments.
He closed his eyes tightly and took a bite.
Vincenzo, seeing what had happened, smiled to himself.
"Papa was right," he thought.
Arm over arm and hand over hand
the stinky meat sandwich moved around the table.
It reached its way to Rita
who took a bite, chewed, and stopped.

"It's not bad. It's not bad!" she whispered to Paul
and handed the one small bite left to Vincenzo.
He popped it into his mouth and reached into his lunch bag
for the anisette cookies and orange juice.

Chicken Soup with Rice
by
Maurice Sendak

JANUARY

In January it's so nice
while slipping on the sliding ice
to sip hot chicken soup with rice.
Sipping once   sipping twice
sipping chicken soup with rice.

FEBRUARY

In February
it will be
my snowman's
anniversary
with cake for him
and soup for me!
Happy once
happy twice
happy chicken soup
with rice.

MARCH

In March the wind
blows down the door
and spills my soup
upon the floor.
It laps it up
and roars for more.
Blowing once
blowing twice
blowing chicken soup
with rice.

APRIL

In April
I will go away
to far off Spain
or old Bombay
and dream about
hot soup all day.
Oh my oh once
oh my oh twice
oh my oh
chicken soup
with rice.

MAY

In May
I truly think it best
to be a robin
lightly dressed
concocting soup
inside my nest.
Mix it once
mix it twice
mix that chicken soup
with rice.

JUNE

In June
I saw a charming group
of roses all begin
to droop.
I pepped them up
with chicken soup!
Sprinkle once
sprinkle twice
sprinkle chicken soup
with rice.

JULY

In July
I'll take a peep
into the cool
and fishy deep
where chicken soup
is selling cheap.
Selling once
selling twice
selling chicken soup
with rice.

In August
it will be so hot
I will become
a cooking pot
cooking soup of course.
Why not?
Cooking once
cooking twice
cooking chicken soup
with rice.

In September
for a while
I will ride
a crocodile
down the
chicken soupy Nile.
Paddle once
paddle twice
paddle chicken soup
with rice.

OCTOBER

In October
I'll be host
to witches, goblins
and a ghost.
I'll serve them
chicken soup
on toast.
Whoopy once
whoopy twice
whoopy chicken soup
with rice.

NOVEMBER

In November's
gusty gale
I will flop
my flippy tail
and spout hot soup.
I'll be a whale!
Spouting once
spouting twice
spouting chicken soup
with rice.

DECEMBER

In December I will be
a baubled bangled Christmas tree
with soup bowls draped all over me.
Merry once   merry twice
merry chicken soup with rice.

The Surprise Sandwich
by
Red Lane

Sometimes when I go out to school or to work
or to just anywhere and I can't come home
for lunch, well I just take a lunch with me
in a paper bag or something.

My favourite lunch to take with me is an Anything sandwich
made out of bread and anything else
like peanut-butter and jam or jam and peanut-butter.

Sometimes my friends bring their lunch too
and they all have different sandwiches.
One friend brought a garlic sandwich once
and another friend brought a brown sugar sandwich
and one friend even brought a mashed potato sandwich.

My best friend always brings a Surprise sandwich
that his mother makes for him
and doesn't tell him what's in it.
And one day his mother didn't put anything
in his Surprise sandwich and when he took a bite
he was Really surprised.

Sometimes I take other food in my lunch
  like an orange or a piece of cake or even a banana
that I have to be careful not to squish.

And sometimes my friends bring other food
in their lunch too.
One friend brought an onion once
and another friend brought a lemon
and one friend brought an apple with a worm in it.

My best friend always brings Surprise food
that his mother wraps up for him
and doesn't tell what it is.
And one day his mother wrapped up a fresh Egg
for him instead of hardboiled
and when he tried to peel it
he was Really surprised.

Of course the very best thing about any lunch
is having a lunch to eat.
And sometimes when I'm eating lunch I think
what about all the people everywhere
who have no lunch to eat and maybe no supper
and maybe not even a snack before going to bed.

And when I think about that
my lunch doesn't taste too good
thinking about all the kids and people everywhere
who haven't even got a lunch to taste so good.

And when I think about that
I don't want to even eat my lunch
and I just sit around wondering if there's anything
I can do to help those kids and people
like maybe mail them a sandwich or something
and I guess that would be silly.

But sometimes I wonder about it all day.
And I guess a lot of kids and people wonder about it.
And then I seem to forget about it by suppertime.
And I guess a lot of kids and people forget about it.

Well I guess if you were to stop and think about it
you would find that the lunches kids and people have
are only as important as the lunches
kids and people have not. If you know what I mean.
Do you know what I mean?

How Trouble Made the Monkey Eat Pepper

as told by
Rita Cox

Crick, crack.
Monkey break me back.

Ma Minnie lived in a tiny village in Trinidad,
on the Islands. All the children around knew Ma Minnie,
for she made her living selling the most delicious cakes
and sweets, which she made herself. Oh, the smells
that came from Ma Minnie's backyard, where she baked
and cooked all the day long!

Once a week this old lady went to market to buy molasses
for making her coconut cakes. One day she started out late.
By the time she was on her way back home, the sun was high
in the sky and she became hot and more tired than usual.

So there Ma Minnie was, walking through the tall trees
with a gourd of molasses on her head. She stubbed her foot
against a stone, and the gourd fell crashing to the ground
with the molasses spreading out all over.

Poor Ma Minnie! She picked up a piece of the gourd
to scoop up the thick, sweet syrup. She wailed, "Ah me,
what trouble! Look at my trouble!"—all the while
licking her fingers. Then she continued sadly,
"I'll have to go right back to market. Ah me!"

A monkey, sitting on a tree limb above, observed
what was going on. He was curious, especially when he saw
Ma Minnie licking her fingers. When Ma Minnie had left,
he scurried down and tasted the molasses.
"If this is trouble, then trouble is sweet. I'd like
to have some myself. I think I'll go into town and buy some."

So Brer Monkey dressed himself in his scissortail coat
and his fine top hat, and he set out for the market.
He stopped at the first shop. The shopkeeper was having
a lively conversation with some friends when Brer Monkey said,
"I've come to buy some trouble."

Silence.

"Trouble? Do you know what trouble is?" asked the shopkeeper.

"Yes man, I know what trouble is
and I want to buy all you have."

"All right," replied the shopkeeper. "Remember,
you asked for it," and he went to the back of the shop
while his customers giggled. Brer Monkey glared at them all.

The shopkeeper returned with a big bag.
"Here is your trouble, sir. Now will you pay me, please?"
Brer Monkey paid the shopkeeper, took the bag, and left.

"Oh," he thought as he went along, "this trouble is heavier than I thought. What strange sounds are coming from this bag, and it is so hot. I can't wait to find a quiet place to stop and enjoy some of this trouble."

At last he came to a clearing under some trees. He put his bag down, removed his hat, and licked his lips in anticipation. Then he sat down and untied the bag.

Out rushed three fierce, hungry dogs. Poor Brer Monkey! He rushed up the nearest tree to escape from the attackers, who stayed at the bottom, barking and yelping.

Oh, Brer Monkey was so hot in his fine clothes— and so hungry, for he had eaten nothing all that day.

The dogs stayed beneath the tree for a long time, and Brer Monkey grew hungrier and hungrier. The dogs didn't go away.

Finally, in desperation, Brer Monkey leaned over and picked up a fruit from an overhanging branch and hungrily stuffed it into his mouth. How could he know it was a hot pepper tree? Oh, did it burn! Oh, did it hurt! How Brer Monkey suffered!

At last, the dogs went away and Brer Monkey rushed down and threw himself, fine clothes and all, into a nearby stream. And that is how trouble made the monkey eat pepper.

I jumped on the wire
and the wire bend,
And that's the way
the story end.

Street Song
by
Myra Cohn Livingston

O, I have been walking
with a bag of potato chips,
me and potato chips
munching along,

Walking alone
eating potato chips,
big old potato chips
crunching along,

Walking along
munching potato chips,
me and potato chips
lunching along.

Apple War
by
Frank Asch

One, two, three, four,
They marched like soldiers past my door,
One, two, three, four,
They marched into the grocery store,
One, two, three, four,
They spent a dollar, not a cent more.
One, two, three, four,
They bought apples rotten to the core,
One, two, three, four,
They marched out of the grocery store,
One, two, three, four,
They marched like soldiers past my door,
One, two, three, four,
They had a rotten apple war.

Food for Thought

by
David Booth and Meguido Zola

In the kitchen
from the fridge
to the table
in a bowl
on a spoon
to the mouth
through the teeth
past the gums

Look out stomach,
here it comes!

My Mouth
by
Arnold Adoff

My Mouth
      stays shut
            but
food   just
finds
     a way
         my tongue says
we are
      full today
      but
        teeth just
           grin
      and
      say
        come in
i am always hungry

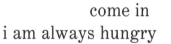

Revenge
by
Myra Cohn Livingston

When I find out
who took
the last cookie

out of the jar
and left
me a bunch of

stale old messy
crumbs, I'm
going to take

me a handful
and crumb
up *someone's* bed.

Song of the Pop-Bottlers

by
Maurice Bishop

POP bottles pop-bottles
  in pop shops:
The pop-bottles POP bottles
  poor POP drops.

When POP drops pop-bottles
  pop-bottles plop!
Pop-bottle-tops topple!
  POP mops slop!

Stop! POP'll drop bottle!
  Stop, POP, stop!
When POP bottles pop-bottles,
  pop-bottles pop!

Where Seasons Change
by
Fran Newman and Claudette Boulanger

I'm glad I don't live
Where it's sun and rain,
Then sun
And rain
Again, again!

I'm glad that I live
Where there's ice and snow,
And fall
And spring
And summer glow.

I'm glad that I live
Where seasons change;
I like
My world
To rearrange!

The Sleighs of Old Montreal
by
Carlo Italiano

When I was a boy
there were a lot of sleighs in Montreal.
I could tell what sleigh was passing my house
by the sound of its bells;
tinkling, jingling, bonging, or clunking.

Our street was great for sleigh-watching!
As soon as I could hold a pencil,
I started drawing these sleighs.
I don't see them much anymore;
but I remember.

From THE SLEIGHS OF MY CHILDHOOD/LES TRAINEAUX DE MON ENFANCE © 1974 Carlo Italiano published by Tundra Books.

The Milk Sleigh

Milk sleighs were out on the streets before daylight.
Sometimes, they followed the first snowplough.

The milk horse knew every stop on the way.
While the milkman delivered milk to one house,
the horse moved on to the next.

On very cold mornings,
the milk froze before we took it inside.
A solid, white neck stuck out of the bottle.
It was a poor child's ice cream.

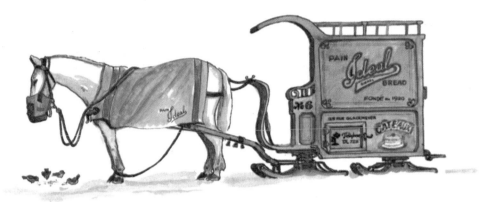

The Bread Sleigh

The bread was delivered every day.
The best thing about the bread sleigh
was the little folding step at the back.
It made a good seat for us to steal rides on.

The "Star" Sleigh

This sleigh delivered the "Montreal Star" newspapers
to newsstands all over the city.
The newsstands sold each paper for two cents.

The Farmer's Sleigh

Many wonderful sleighs came to the markets of Montreal.
But the farmer's sleigh was my favourite.
The simple sleigh and harness were handmade on the farm.
The horse that pulled the sleigh was the same horse
that did all the other farm chores.

The driver always wore a grey winter coat
that was tied at the waist with a wool belt.
The belt had his own special pattern on it,
that was woven on the farm.

I don't ever remember seeing a driver
without a pipe in his mouth.

The Fire-Hose Sleigh

The Fire Department used wagons changed into sleighs.
At the station, everything was kept at the ready.
When the alarm rang, the horses moved
into the harnesses like lightening.
Everything was tightened.
The runners of the sleigh sat
on greased tracks. Within a few moments,
the horses exploded out of the station.

The Chip Wagon

In winter, the chip wagons changed
their wheels for sleigh runners.
But we still called them "chip wagons,"
never chip sleighs.
French-fried potatoes and hot dogs
from the chip wagon tasted best in winter.
The chips were served in paper cones.
They were always greasy
and always nice and warm when you touched them.
For an extra dime, you could get hot buttered popcorn
and roasted peanuts in the shell.

While the whistle on the roof blew,
and the windows fogged up,
the chipman shook the basket of his deep fryer.
He turned valves, pumped fuel,
and gave out lots of happiness.

The Sightseeing Sleigh

The sightseeing sleigh is the only sleigh
that you can still see in Montreal.
All winter it winds up and down
the roads of Mount Royal,
taking passengers to the top of the mountain
for a special view of the city.

I can remember when a whole team of horses
pulled the sightseeing sleigh.
The sleighs were bright red, green, or blue.
They had shiny rails and handholds.
They carried buffalo robes or bearskins
to keep the passengers warm and snug.

One thing hasn't changed.
A ride up Mount Royal by sleigh
is still one of the happiest things
to do in Montreal during winter.

My Feet Roll
Illustrated by
Winnie Mertens

...my feet roll

How Six Found Christmas

by
Trina Schart Hyman

Once upon a time there was a little girl
who had never heard of Christmas
and therefore did not know what it was.
By chance one day she happened to meet an old wise woman
who told her that there was such a thing.
But the wise woman did not elaborate on the matter,
so the little girl was left as ignorant as before,
yet with a great curiosity.

Being a sensible child, she decided that the best way
to find out what a Christmas was would be to go
and find one and have a look for herself.
So she set out, as many others have done before her,
for the Great Snow Forest of the North,
to look for Christmas.

She travelled for two days and two nights,
and on the morning of the third day she chanced
to meet a large gray cat who was sitting
at the edge of the forest shaking her paws
on account of the snow.

"Where are you going, my child," asked the cat,
"and where are your mittens?"
This cat was a straightforward, motherly soul.

"I am going to find a Christmas," said the little girl,
"and my mittens are in my pocket."

"What on earth is a Christmas?" asked the cat, astonished.
"I have never heard of such a thing. What does it feel like?
Is it comfortable and warm? Does it have fur?
Is it wet, or dry? Is it cold and sharp and smooth like ice,
or is it prickly warm velvet like summer grass?
Tell me quickly, for I am curious, being a cat."

"Bless you, Tabby, I don't know what it feels like,"
answered the child. "I myself have never felt a Christmas,
which is why I am looking for one. If you are really
so curious, why don't you come along with me?
Then, when I find one, you may feel it for yourself."

To this the cat agreed, and they set off together
through the Great Snow Forest. They had not gone far
before they met a sad-faced hound, nosing his way
from tree to tree.

"I beg your pardon," said the hound,
"but did either of you ladies happen to see
a rabbit pass this way not long ago?"

"No," said the little girl, "I have seen no rabbit at all.
But in your hunting, did you happen to come across
a Christmas?"

The dog sat down and gazed at her mournfully.
"You know," he said, "I'm not really sure.
As a matter of fact, I am not at all sure
I know what a Christmas is.
What does a Christmas smell like? Is it musty
and strong like rabbits and squirrels? Does it smell
as delicious and comforting as cooking meat,
or as ancient and frightening as old cellars?
Does it smell like a human baby, or a river bank,
or perhaps like rotting leaves?"

"Bless you, Dog," said the child, "I can't tell you
what a Christmas smells like,
for I myself have never smelled one.
If you are really interested, why don't you come along
with us, and when we find a Christmas you may smell
for yourself."

Having by now given up the rabbit, the hound decided
that this was not such a bad idea, and he fell in step
with the cat and the little girl.

They spent the night in a deserted castle,
and on the morning of the fourth day the three travellers
met a great red hawk perched on the limb of a fir tree.

"Halt!" snapped the hawk. Since he was very regal-looking,
they all did as they were told. "I have been watching you
from afar for a day and a night, and I demand to know
where you are going and why you are going there."

"Well of course," said the little girl. "We are looking
for a Christmas. It was I who wanted to find one first,
you see, because I don't know what it is. And then
my friends the cat and the dog decided that they would like
to find a Christmas, too. So, although we don't know
exactly where we are going, at any rate
that is why we are going there."

"I see," said the hawk, frowning and moving from one foot
to the other. "Well, I can tell you right now
that such a thing does not exist. If it did,
I would have seen it on my travels. What does
a Christmas look like? Does it glitter? Does it move?
Quickly or slowly? Is it dark or bright? What colour is it?
Is it round and fuzzy or is it flat and clear?
Does it change its shape, or does it remain the same?"

"Bless you, Hawk," said the little girl, "I can't answer
your questions because I myself have never seen a Christmas,
or even heard it described. If you really want to know
what it looks like, why don't you come along with us,
and when we find one you may see for yourself."

After a moment's thought, the hawk agreed to come.
As the others walked along he flew behind them
at a sedate height.

They travelled all that day. Just as evening was coming on
they met a wise old fox, who pricked up his ears
and grinned when he saw them.

"Whither away?" said the fox,
who fancied himself an old-fashioned gentleman.

"Good evening," said the little girl.
"We are travelling through the Great Snow Forest,
looking for a Christmas. Do you happen to know
where we might find one?"

"A Christmas, a Christmas," murmured the fox,
looking clever. "No, my dear, I can't say that I know
exactly where you could find one at this time of year.
Perhaps in the summer yes. A Christmas, you say?
Now let me see....Perhaps I know it by another name.
Would you describe the thing for me?
What does it taste like? Is there lots of juicy blood?
Is it sweet, or salty, or sour, or peppery? Is it crisp?
Does it go crunch when one bites it, or does it slip
between one's teeth and slide down one's throat?
Is it spicy and rich, or is it bland and wholesome?"

"Bless you, old Fox," said the child.
"I can't tell you how it tastes for I have never eaten
a Christmas. If you really wish to know
all those things, why don't you come along with us?
If we find one, you may take a taste.
But only a nibble, mind you!"

As the fox was rather hungry, even a nibble seemed better
to him than nothing, so he readily agreed to go
along with the others.

The whole of the next day they travelled through the forest,
searching for a Christmas. In the late afternoon
they met a mockingbird who was amusing himself
by pretending he was a nightingale.

"Hello, hello!" he said. "What have we here?
What brings so many creatures this far
into the Great Snow Forest at once?"

"Oh Mockingbird," said the little girl,
who was by now getting weary and discouraged,
"we are looking for a Christmas. Do you know
where we might find one?"

"A Christmas!" exclaimed the Mockingbird,
and whistled long and low. "What the devil is that?
Tell me what it sounds like, and I'll tell you where to find one.
Does it tinkle? Does it shriek? Does it boom and roar,
or does it titter and squeak? Does it laugh? Does it sob?
Does it use one note, or many? Is it music, or is it noise?"

"Bless you, Mockingbird," said the child,
"that I can't tell you, for I have never heard
a Christmas. If you wish to know what it sounds like,
I advise you to come along with us, for if we ever find one,
then you may hear it." And so he did.

And it came to pass that on the evening of the fifth day
they came upon an old green bottle, dropped in the snow
by some lonely hunter, perhaps, or a long-dead, frozen king.
There it lay, solitary and startling in the Great Snow Forest.
And the rays of the setting sun shone on the green glass,
and it became as fire and ice, and as the sea and summer.

"Well," said the little girl, "I believe this is possibly
what we are looking for. It is certainly very beautiful,
and I somehow feel that this is a Christmas."

The big gray cat went up to the bottle and put her paw
on it. Then she rubbed her whiskers against it,
and lay down next to it. "It is smooth and cold,"
she said. "It has a silky and yet a hard feel to it.
Not exactly my cup of tea, but yes, I believe
that you are right. This must be a Christmas."

Next the hound went nosing up to the bottle, and sniffed it
all over. He put his nose to the opening. Then he looked
worriedly at the little girl. "It smells old," he said.
"It smells of past memories, half-forgotten things,
both happy and sad. I can't say that it smells delicious,
but it certainly does have a smell all its own. Musty,
sort of. I guess this is what you were looking for."

Then the hawk flew down and perched on the child's shoulder,
and gazed at the bottle with his most formidable gaze.
"Madam," he finally said, "it is a beautiful object.
Pleasing shape, lovely colour and a sort of inner fire
that gives it a most interesting glitter.
Both round and clear. No real movement there, of course,
but it has a definite charm nevertheless. I would say
without a doubt that this is a Christmas,
and quite a good example of one at that."

Now the fox went over and nibbled at the neck of the bottle.
"Certainly no crunch there, and not any juice, either,"
he grumbled. "Tastes of snow, and winter air,
and maybe just a little salt." He was rather disappointed.
"Yes, I suppose this is a Christmas, my dear.
But if I were you, I'd let it sit until summer.
By then it may have gotten some of its flavour back."

The Mockingbird just whispered,
"No sound at all. How remarkable! No sound at all!"
He shook his head sadly for a while,
then he gave a low whistle and flew away.

The little girl took up the bottle, brushed the snow
from its sides, and put it under her coat.
Then she started on the long journey back home.

The hawk, after expounding a little
on the virtues of the Christmas, flew off
to the Great Finn Forests to hunt for weasels.
The fox, after a day of travelling
thanked the little girl for a pleasant experience,
bowed low over her hand, and trotted off
to try and get a decent meal somewhere.

The dog and the cat walked her the rest of the way home, and they parted with promises to see one another often, or at least write.

The little girl took the bottle and set it on her table. Then she filled it with branches of red berries, and soft green pine. And the evening stars shone through the window and onto the green glass, making it glisten softly. And lo! It was Christmas!

Christmas is not only where you find it;
it's what you make of it.

Wishers
by
Dolores Hind

Take a candle warm and bright.
Gently blow the flickering light,
And wish a wish.

Take a star from a starry sky.
Watch it; follow it with your eye,
And wish a wish.

Do Not Open Until Christmas!

by
Jean Little

Gregory wished he had not learned how to tell time.
Last Christmas, he had raced in and wakened Mother
and Daddy right away, before it was beginning to be light
outside. This year, he had to look at the clock on his dresser.
Ten minutes past seven!

"No getting up till eight o'clock,"
Mother had ordered the night before.

Gregory had groaned, but then he had given in and agreed
because she looked so tired. How was he to know
he would be wide awake at ten past seven?

He curled up again under the covers and began the long wait.
Maybe if he counted. . . .He counted to one hundred three times.
Then he shot out of the bed to check.
Sixteen minutes past seven!

Gregory could not get back into bed this time.
He just couldn't! There must be something he could *do*
to make the time pass. Then he remembered the three gifts
hidden away in his closet. He had kept them there
so his parents and Holly would not have a chance to guess
at what was inside. Gregory knew all about shaking presents
and squeezing them. He had been doing it all week.

Now Christmas morning had really come, and it was time to put
the three presents under the tree with the others. Maybe by the
time he had them arranged just so, it would be eight o'clock.

He had made a pencil holder out of popsicle sticks for Daddy,
and Mother had shown him how to string pieces of macaroni
into a necklace for Holly. Holly was four. Better than anything,
she loved dressing up and pretending she was a ''grown-up
person.'' Gregory grinned, hearing already how she would speak
with delight when she saw what he had for her.

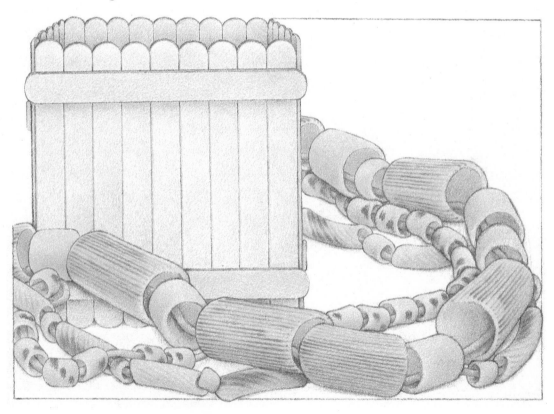

But his mother's present was the best. As he took out
the box that held it, his heart beat faster.
Would she like it? Would she see how special it was?

He had made her a bird. It had taken him a long time.
He had found bits of wood the right shape
and glued them together, one by one. When it was done,
Daddy had let him spray it with silver paint.
The bird could not stand up by itself,
but, if you leaned it against something,
it seemed to stand, with wings spread,
as though it were about to fly.

Gregory thought it the most beautiful thing
he had ever seen.

Carrying the gifts, he started tiptoeing across the hall.
He paused at Holly's door. It hardly seemed fair
going downstairs without her.

She would giggle, though, and waken the others.
Besides, he was only slipping down for one minute.
He would put the things under the tree. . .
and maybe just check to see if something new
had been put with his pile of presents. . . .

There *was* something new! It was right on top—
and it was huge. Kneeling quickly to look,
Gregory almost dropped his mother's bird.

He was too excited to arrange the three gifts carefully,
as he had meant to do. He put them down
without noticing where and reached for the big box.

Then, as he lifted it, testing to see how heavy it was,
he saw that one corner of the wrapping paper was loose.
As he slid his finger in, under the edge,
he saw the sticker. *Do Not Open Until Christmas*!

"But it is Christmas, really," he said out loud
to the quiet room. "Just this one won't matter."

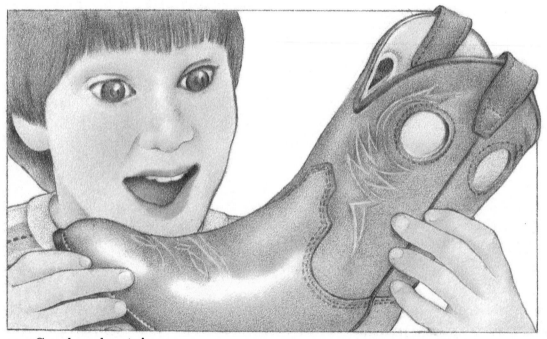

Cowboy boots!
He could not believe it. He had wanted them for so long.
He had asked Mother before his last birthday, even.
She had priced them.

"They're too expensive, Gregory," she had told him.

He had heard how sorry she was, in her voice. He had known
she wanted him to have them almost as badly as he did himself.
She must have found a way!

He pulled them on. They felt strange on his bare feet
but they were exactly his size.
Oh, beautiful, wonderful boots!

He did not plan to go on and open the next present.
There were so many things waiting, though.
His hands reached out by themselves.
A Scrabble game! A baseball glove!

The package under the book felt like something to wear.
Gregory skipped that one.

The next one, though, he had wondered about for days.
It had such an interesting rattle. A chess set of his own!
Gregory glowed. He had been learning to play
with Daddy's set, but he had wanted a cheap one
he could take to school. He was the only boy in his class
who had started to learn to play chess.

He had just opened the last box when Mother found him.
"Gregory!" she cried out.

At once he knew he had done a terrible thing.
He tried to explain, to make her listen
to the excuses he had been telling himself.
"They say *Do Not Open Until Christmas* . . .
and it *is* Christmas," he stammered.
"You told me not to wake you. . . ."
It was like being caught inside a bad dream.
She was so angry—and so sad.

"It's not the end of the world, Margaret," Daddy told her.

"How could he? How *could* he?" was all she would answer.

Holly saved Christmas for them. She was starry-eyed
with wonder and excitement. Mother had to hide her anger
so it would not spoil the brightness of Holly's morning.

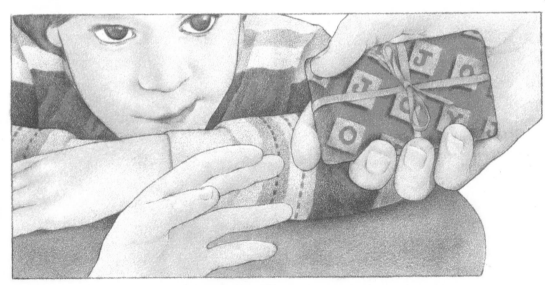

Gregory sat in the big chair. He watched the other three
opening their gifts. He felt left out and lonely.
He still could not understand his mother.
He was the one with no presents left to open.
It was his own Christmas he had ruined, not hers.

Then he saw her pick up the box with the bird in it.
Gregory tensed, waiting, watching.

Slowly, she undid the wrapping. She lifted the lid.
Then, at last, it was out in her hands,
his silver bird with its wings set for flight.
"Oh, Gregory!" she whispered.

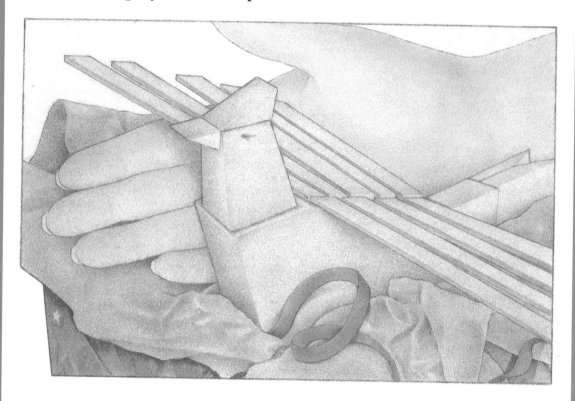

He stared at her. Her face was shining with joy,
with love. He could not move. He saw her put the bird
down gently, propping it with care so that it looked
ready to soar away. Then she turned and stretched out
her arms to him. "It's all right," she murmured,
"the bird is so lovely. . . ."

With a gasp of relief, Gregory ran to her. She hugged him
exactly as if he had not stirred out of his bed till eight o'clock.
He knew, then, what he had done.
He had taken away from her the moment of giving.

He had seen the glow on her face when she opened the box
and first saw the bird, but she had not shared his delight
in the boots he still could not believe were really his.
"I'm sorry, Mother," he said, into her shoulder.

"Gregory," his father said suddenly, "here's something for you."

It was the one he had not bothered with,
the one that felt like clothes. Gregory's hands shook
as he pulled the scotch tape loose. He had been right.
It was a pair of pajamas. They were striped ones
like those he had on. They were not a bit exciting at all.

He looked up at his mother and struggled to put all his joy
over the cowboy boots into his face.
"Mother," he said, "they are just what I wanted most!"

Mother laughed understandingly.
"Merry Christmas, Gregory!" she said.

If I want I can give it to a friend

by
Ruth Krauss

some grass

and some ocean

and some dark for daytime

and some sun for nighttime

and a hug—

I put them down together

on a piece of paper

—I could hold it in my hand

—I could keep it in my pocket

you could roll it in a little ball
and poke it in a shell

A Wart Snake in a Fig Tree

by
George Mendoza

On the first day of Christmas
my true love gave to me
a wart snake in a fig tree.

On the second day of Christmas
my true love gave to me
two bags of soot
and a wart snake in a fig tree.

On the third day of Christmas
my true love gave to me
three cobwebs,
two bags of soot,
and a wart snake in a fig tree.

On the fourth day of Christmas
my true love gave to me
four raven wings,
three cobwebs,
two bags of soot,
and a wart snake in a fig tree.

On the fifth day of Christmas
my true love gave to me
five useless things,
four raven wings,
three cobwebs,
two bags of soot,
and a wart snake in a fig tree.

On the sixth day of Christmas
my true love gave to me
six shadows lurking,
five useless things,
four raven wings,
three cobwebs,
two bags of soot,
and a wart snake in a fig tree.

On the seventh day of Christmas
my true love gave to me
seven ghouls acaroling,
six shadows lurking,
five useless things,
four raven wings,
three cobwebs,
two bags of soot,
and a wart snake in a fig tree.

On the eighth day of Christmas
my true love gave to me
eight snow wolves wailing,
seven ghouls acaroling,
six shadows lurking,
five useless things,
four raven wings,
three cobwebs,
two bags of soot,
and a wart snake in a fig tree.

On the ninth day of Christmas
my true love gave to me
nine nightmares galloping,
eight snow wolves wailing,
seven ghouls acaroling,
six shadows lurking,
five useless things,
four raven wings,
three cobwebs,
two bags of soot,
and a wart snake in a fig tree.

On the tenth day of Christmas
my true love gave to me
ten ground hogs grinning,
nine nightmares galloping,
eight snow wolves wailing,
seven ghouls acaroling,
six shadows lurking,
five useless things,
four raven wings,
three cobwebs,
two bags of soot,
and a wart snake in a fig tree.

On the eleventh day of Christmas
my true love gave to me
eleven lizards boiling,
ten ground hogs grinning,
nine nightmares galloping,
eight snow wolves wailing,
seven ghouls acaroling,
six shadows lurking,
five useless things,
four raven wings,
three cobwebs,
two bags of soot,
and a wart snake in a fig tree.

On the twelfth day of Christmas
my true love gave to me
twelve days of raining,
eleven lizards boiling,
ten ground hogs grinning,
nine nightmares galloping,
eight snow wolves wailing,
seven ghouls acaroling,
six shadows lurking,
five useless things,
four raven wings,
three cobwebs,
two bags of soot,
and a wart snake in a fig tree.

Day and Night: How They Came to Be

by
Knud Rasmussen

In those times
when just saying a word
could make something happen,
there was no light on earth yet.
Everything was in darkness all the time,
people lived in darkness.

A fox and a hare had an argument,
each saying his magic word:
"Darkness," said the fox,
for he wanted it to be dark
so he could go hunting.

"Day," said the hare,
for he wanted daylight
so he could find good grass to eat.

The hare won: His word was more powerful
and he got his wish:
Day came, replacing night.
But the word of the fox was powerful too
and when day was over, night came,
and from then on they took turns with each other,
the nightime of the fox
following the daytime of the hare.

The Arctic: What Lives There

by
Lee Pennock Huntington

In the Arctic, most of the land is always frozen.
Deep crevices split the hard rough surface of the snow.
There are towering white mountains, but no trees.
At the edge of the polar lands are the cold polar seas,
full of moving chunks of ice, called pack ice.
During the long winter, the sky is dark day and night.
Everywhere you look, there is snow and ice.
What can live in such frozen unprotected places?

Many kinds of wildlife make their home in the icy waters
and on the snow-covered land of the Arctic.
Small growing things called plankton fill the polar seas
and float together to make green pastures
for hungry sea creatures. Even smaller
is the one-celled plant called the diatom,
smaller than the dot at the end of this sentence.
Billions of diatoms live in the plankton.

Diatoms in plankton are food for krill.
Krill are tiny lobsterlike creatures which move
through the water with five pairs of "paddles."
In summer, the open water of the Arctic seas is filled
with swiftly paddling krill. In winter, krill live
on plankton under the ice. Fish, clams, seabirds, whales,
walruses, and seals all depend on krill for survival.

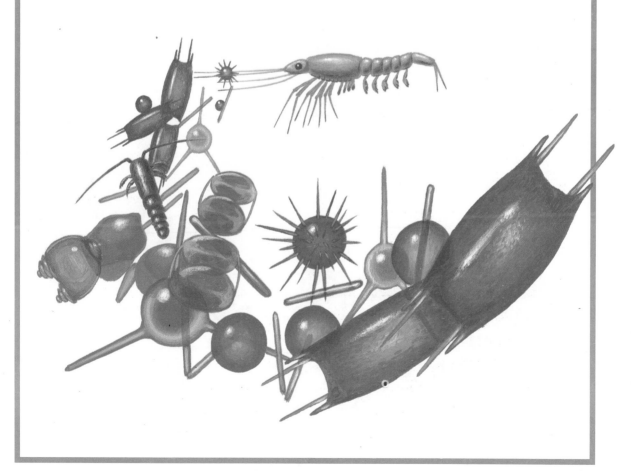

In the Arctic, seals live on the moving pack ice.
When they hunt for krill, they dive deep into the water.
They live in the water under thick layers of ice and snow.
Their sleek shape helps them swim well,
but they must come up often to breathe. In winter,
they find cracks in the ice and stick their muzzles
out for air, or they make breathing holes
by gnawing the ice or bashing it with their heads.

Seals can endure such cold temperatures
because they have thick layers of fat, called blubber,
under their heavy sleek fur. In the spring, mother seals
climb out on the ice, where their babies are born.
All summer long they sun and nap on the ice,
diving for krill.

In the Arctic, seals have to watch out for polar bears.
Seals are a polar bear's main food. The bear stalks
silently across the ice to attack the unwary ones.
In winter the bear waits beside a seal's breathing hole
to strike with steely claws, dragging the seal out
the instant its muzzle appears. The bear's shoulder muscles
are so powerful it can crush a seal by hugging it.
When seals are scarce, a polar bear will search for them,
riding to new areas on big chunks of floating ice
called floes.

Bears dig dens in the snow where they hibernate
during the worst part of the winter.
Protected by their heavy fur, they live off their fat.
Sheltered from the weather, the cubs are born in the den
where the mother bear keeps them warm.

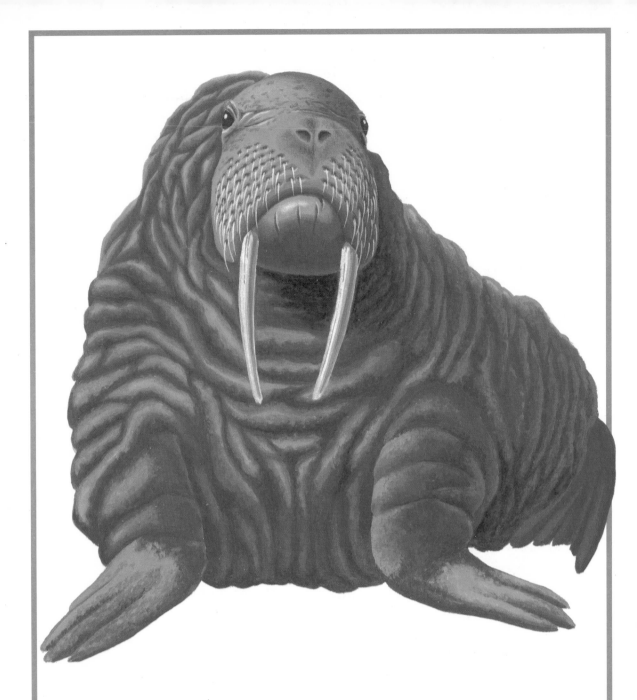

The walrus is too big for a polar bear to attack.
A walrus is so big it needs to eat thousands of krill
and clams each day. With its tusks it scrapes off shellfish
from under the ice. Its thick whiskers help it feel around
in the water to find krill. Layers of blubber protect
walruses when they lie out on the ice in winter wind.

Walruses live together in large herds,
and their roars and bellows make them the noisiest creatures
in the Arctic.

Only the southern edge of the Arctic Circle is not frozen
all year long. It is called the tundra, a place
of low-growing plants, wet bogs, and dry winds.

An iron-hard layer of earth lies beneath the tundra.
It is always frozen. During the Arctic winter,
from November to February, the sun does not appear at all.
The tundra is a vast expanse of snow.

Gradually the sun returns and by May the tundra snow
begins to melt and leaves a thin layer of mud.
Mosses and flat lichen grow on rocks. Lichen eats away
at the rock, which slowly crumbles and becomes soil.
The soil is the home for long, shallow roots of plants
that grow close to the ground, sheltered from
frigid winds.

On the tundra, dwarf willows have branches
no bigger than your finger. Bees, spiders, and beetles
are at home in this world of small tough flowers
and grasses. Melting snow leaves pools and puddles
where mosquitoes breed. They hover thickly in the air
at midsummer over an expanse of dandelions,
buttercups, and golden Arctic poppies.

The tundra is crossed by rivers and dotted by lakes.
Streams flow from inland mountains to the coast.
In summer, shorebirds migrate from their winter homes
to the rocky beaches of the Arctic. Here they make nests,
finding all the krill they need.

One of these birds is the snow goose,
whose powerful black-tipped wings carry it
hundreds of kilometres north to its nesting place.

Land birds hunt insects and small animals.
Many tundra birds have feathers speckled and mottled
in colours matching the moss, pebbles, and old grass.
A ptarmigan sitting still and her eggs laid
in a grassy nest are safe from sharp-eyed tundra predators.
White birds, like the great snowy owl, are safest
when there is snow on the ground.

The tundra is home for many animals.
Herds of caribou move across the plain, eating lichen.
The caribou's long legs and wide hooves help it pick
its way over ice. Polar wolves hunt the old,
sick or young ones in a caribou flock.

Musk oxen graze on willows and grasses through the summer.
During the longer winter, they live mostly on their own fat,
and heavy fleece protects them from cold.
Adult oxen form a ring to shelter the calves,
whose coats are not so thick.

All the animals of the Arctic have learned to adapt
to their surroundings. Arctic hares have noses
keen enough to smell plants under a foot of snow.
They scrape with sharp teeth and claws to find willow twigs
and lichen to eat. White Arctic hares are impossible to see
against the snow. The coats of Arctic foxes and weasels
change to white in the winter.

A cousin of the mouse and the hamster lives
in the Arctic. It is the little brown lemming,
the chief food of many tundra animals. Lemmings dig
underground tunnels, breaking up the tundra soil
so that plant roots can take hold. In summer
there are many plants for lemmings to eat.
In winter they nibble on mats of willow and roots
beneath the snow cover.

Lemmings breed rapidly. There are so many of them
that sometimes they use up their winter supply of food
early and pop up in March to look for more.
Then owls, hawks and gulls, foxes and weasels pounce
on them. But the lemmings continue to multiply.
The whole tundra is dug up as they search
for more food. They chew up everything in sight
and ruin the feeding grounds for other animals.

Many lemmings starve. Others travel many kilometres,
frantically looking for food. Sometimes an army of lemmings
rushes to the edge of the sea and drowns. Birds and animals
that depend on lemmings for food begin to starve.

Snowy owls and hawks go hungry.
Weasels wriggle into lemming holes
to track down those that are left.
Foxes, too big to enter the tunnels, starve.

A few lemmings will always live and start families
next spring. For several years they will be able to find
enough food. Then the time comes when once more
there are too many lemmings.

It can be very beautiful in the Arctic,
especially when the sky is lit by northern lights.
These lights, called aurora borealis, are gases
which show up as colours, usually glowing yellow or green,
sometimes red and blue. Like curtains slowly opening
and closing, they spread across the black sky.

If you could keep warm and find enough to eat,
you would enjoy watching the aurora borealis
all the long Arctic winter.

Magic Words to Feel Better
by
Knud Rasmussen

Sea Gull
who flaps his wings
over my head
     in the blue air,

you gull up there
dive down
     come here
take me with you
     in the air!

Wings flash by
my mind's eye
and I'm up there sailing
in the cool air,
     a-a-a-a-a-ah,
       in the air.

The Girl Who Became a Reindeer

retold by
Ronald Melzack

There was once a young girl whose name was Leealaura,
who lived with her mother and father in a small igloo.
Leealaura's father made her toys to play with,
and told her stories during the long winter nights.
Her mother made her fine clothes, and played with her
whenever she had time.

One day Leealaura's father came home with a boy
and a girl whose parents had been lost in a storm.
Leealaura's parents spent almost all of their time
looking after the little children. Her father made
toys for them, and her mother made them clothes.

Leealaura felt that her mother and father no longer loved her.
One day, while her father was preparing for the day's hunt,
and her mother was feeding the two children,
Leealaura put on her clothes and went outside.

It was summertime, and little berry bushes grew
at the sides of the hills. As Leealaura walked
across the hills, she felt more and more unhappy.
Of all things on earth, she thought to herself,
it is worst to be a human being.

As Leealaura wandered about, she saw
a large flock of snow-geese feeding at the hillside.
All around them were berries, green leaves, and seeds.
The snow-geese looked fat and happy.
"Oh, if only I were a snow-goose," said Leealaura,
"I would be happy."

The longer Leealaura watched the snow-geese,
the more she wanted to be one of them. She followed them
as they flew from one berry patch to another. Finally,
the leader of the flock came up to her and asked,
"Why is it, stranger, that you have followed us all day?"

Leealaura answered, "It is because I would like to be
one of you."

And the leader said, "Our lives are not as pleasant
as they may seem to you. Even though we're warm
and have plenty of food, we are always in danger.
We are hunted by birds and animals as well as by men.
Surely you would not like to be one of us."
Leealaura had not thought of these things,
so she gave up the idea of becoming a snow-goose.

Fall came and still Leealaura wandered about. One morning
she saw a pair of rabbits frisking among the willows.
She watched them while they ate and played on the grass.
"I think I would be happy if I were a rabbit,"
thought Leealaura. "I'll follow them and maybe
they will pity me and help me become a rabbit."

As she approached the rabbits, they ran away. She followed
them, but whenever she came near they hopped away.
Then one of the rabbits came to Leealaura and asked,
"Why have you followed us all day?"

And Leealaura answered, "I would like to be a rabbit."

"You wouldn't be happy if you were a rabbit,"
said the rabbit sadly. "We're miserable most of the time.
Big birds hunt us. Foxes and wolves eat us.
Even minks and weasels take our children!
Surely you don't want to be a rabbit!"
Leealaura was convinced by the rabbit's argument
and gave up the idea of becoming a rabbit.

Through the fall and winter Leealaura kept up her search
for a happy life. One day she saw a large herd of reindeer
grazing on the hillside. How happy they looked!
So she started towards the deer in hope
that they might let her become a reindeer.
Yet every time she approached, they moved away
to another spot. She followed them until, at evening,
they climbed over a hill and disappeared from view.

Leealaura climbed to the top of the hill.
Then the leader of the deer came to her and said,
"My girl, why have you followed us all day without a spear?"

"I don't intend to kill any of your people," answered Leealaura.
"I just want to become a reindeer and live with you."

More reindeer came over to see Leealaura.
She looked so sad that they felt sorry for her.
They decided she could become one of them,
and invited her to sleep among them that night.

The next morning Leealaura awoke at sunrise.
All around her were reindeer, kicking away the snow
and eating the grass that they uncovered. She looked at herself,
and to her astonishment, she was a reindeer too!
Now Leealaura was happy for the first time in many months.
She broke through the snow with her sharp hoofs
and ate the tender grass.

Everything went well, except when the herd
was suddenly frightened by wolves and ran away.
Leealaura was always left far behind.
One day the leader asked Leealaura,
"Why can't you keep up with us?"

"It's because I have to look at my feet when I'm running,"
said Leealaura. "I have trouble moving my four feet
all at the same time."

"Never mind your feet when you are running,"
said the leader. "A reindeer looks only at the horizon
when he runs." The next time they were chased by wolves,
Leealaura looked at the horizon, and ran
with the fastest reindeer.

As the happy years went by,
and Leealaura became almost a full grown reindeer,
she began to think about her life as a girl.
She wondered if her mother and father were well,
and if the two children were still with them.
As she thought of these things, Leealaura felt homesick.

One day, she decided to return to her old home,
and went to see the leader of her herd.
The leader whispered secret instructions to Leealaura,
and ended by saying, "It's simple. If you are caught
by Inuit hunters who treat you kindly,
you will turn into a girl again.
But beware of the cruel hunter."

So Leealaura said goodbye to her reindeer friends
and started off towards her old home.
As she got nearer the homes of Inuit hunters,
she passed traps and pitfalls set for reindeer,
but she watched for them and went by them unharmed.
As she approached her father's igloo
she began to think about her mother and father,
forgetting all about the danger around her.
All at once she was caught in a trap
and could go no further.

She knew that it was useless to struggle,
so she lay down and waited quietly.
Soon two young children came up and they saw the reindeer
in the trap. When they saw how sad she looked,
they stroked her head and released her leg from the trap.
They were gentle and kind, and before their very eyes,
the reindeer turned into Leealaura the girl.

Leealaura was overjoyed when her mother and father
recognized her and swept her up in their arms.
Leealaura even welcomed the two orphaned children
as her brother and sister for it was they
who had freed her from the trap and had been so kind
and gentle to her. Leealaura was happy at last.
But whenever she saw a reindeer, she felt sad,
and she remembered the days when she wandered
across the plains and the wind whistled through her antlers.

Pitseolak: Pictures Out of My Life

from recorded interviews by Dorothy Eber

My name is Pitseolak, the Eskimo* word for the sea pigeon.
When I see pitseolaks over the sea, I say,
"There go those lovely birds—that's me flying!"
I have lost the time when I was born
but I am old now—my sons say maybe I am 70.

I became an artist to earn money
but I think I am a real artist. I draw the things
I have never seen, the monsters and spirits,
and I draw the old ways, the things we did
long ago before there were many white men.
I don't know how many drawings I have done
but more than a thousand. There are many Pitseolaks now—
I have signed my name many times.

I have heard that they like my drawings in the south
and I am grateful and happy about it.
To make prints is not easy.
You must think first and this is hard to do.
But I am happy doing the prints. I am going
to keep on doing them until they tell me to stop.
If no one tells me to stop, I shall make them
as long as I am well.

*For many years the native people living in Northern Canada were known as "Eskimos."
This was a name given to them by the Algonquin Indians. It means "eaters of raw meat."
Today, these native people want to be known as "Inuit," which means "the people"
or "the real people." This word comes from their own language, Inuktitut.

A bird from my mind.
Felt pen, 1968

Both in summer and winter we used to move a lot.

Felt pen, 1970

We lived in the old Eskimo way.
We would pick up and go to different camps—
we were free to move anywhere and we lived
in many camps. Sometimes they were near Cape Dorset
and sometimes they were far away.

Safe in the tent.
Felt pen, 1970

In the old days we had different kinds of housing
for the different seasons. We had the igloo,
the *kaamuk*, which is a tent-hut, and the summer tents.
In winter I didn't mind whether we had an igloo
or a kaamuk so long as we had a shelter for our family.

This is how we played tennis.
Felt pen, 1970

This is how we played Eskimo tennis—we threw a ball
underhand and tried to catch it in a sealskin racket.
The racket was called an *autuk*. We made the ball
from caribou skin and stuffed it with something.
We used to play this game a lot, even in winter.

From skins we made buckets to carry water.
Coloured pencil and felt pen, 1967

In the old days I was never done with the sewing.
There were the tents and the kayaks,
and there were all the clothes which were made
from the different skins—seal, caribou and walrus.
From skins we also made cups for drinking
and buckets for carrying water.

A Gift for Kuni
by
Elizabeth Kastner

One winter morning Kuni woke up early,
with his mind buzzing with excitement. Today is my day!
he thought. Father promised to bring me a special gift
for my birthday. I wonder what it will be?

The door to Kuni's room opened softly.
His father and mother stood there smiling at him.
"Happy birthday, Son!" His father led
a handsome Siberian husky dog into the room.
"Here is our birthday gift to you," said father.
"This is Cheno, one of the best lead dogs in the Arctic.
When you two get to know each other, you can travel
on hunting trips together."

Kuni laughed happily when he saw the dog. Cheno stood quietly but proudly, his pointed ears listening to every sound around him. His ice-blue eyes looked at everyone carefully.

"Remember, Kuni," said his father, "you must learn to understand the husky dog before you can build a friendship with him. Especially one like Cheno."

"Why does he seem different from our other sled-dogs?" asked Kuni. "They're huskies too. Is he a different breed?"

"Cheno is a Siberian husky dog, all right," his father answered. "But he is one of the rare ones: a natural born leader. The others grew up learning to be good followers—and that is important too. But once in a while there's a dog that seems wiser and better able to be a leader. Like our new friend Cheno." With a slight move of his hand, Father beckoned to the furry figure by the doorway and Cheno padded toward the side of the bed.

"Like all huskies, Cheno is proud," said Father. "You will have to earn his friendship. A lead dog will not make quick friends with just anyone."

As if he understood, the husky lifted his white and black head ever so slightly and wagged his thick, plumed tail.

"When I traded three new sealskins for him," said Father, "I also promised that Cheno would have a good home with our family. Now I have to leave on a hunting trip with our cousin and his dogs for a few days to find more supplies. So it's up to you, Kuni, to take care of Cheno. Make him feel welcome."

During the hours that followed, Kuni tried in many ways
to make friends with his new dog. But the proud husky
did not allow him or anyone else even to come close.
Kuni would place fresh sealmeat in Cheno's corner of their house,
but the dog would not even move close to the wooden dish.

"You must eat, Cheno," said Kuni. "If you don't eat
or drink, then your strength will fade and you won't be able
to travel with us on hunting trips."

The boy grew more and more worried as the day slipped by.
Cheno just rested on his mat with a faraway look in his eyes.

"You must not worry so," said Kuni's mother, seeing her son's
sad face. "It takes time for Cheno's feelings to come out
and meet ours—just as it is with humans. When Cheno learns
that we need him as much as he needs us, then he'll come to us!"

Later that afternoon, Kuni took the husky outside
to meet his new pack of followers. When Cheno appeared
before them, the other dogs sniffed, yelped, and circled
slowly around him. Knowing that huskies do not bark,
Kuni watched with great interest the special way
these animals seemed to greet each other.

The new husky lead dog raised his head high and gave a long,
deep-throated howl, as if to say: "I am your new leader,
and I have taken charge of all of you from now on.
No matter who you are, or how long you have been with the group,
you are now bound to follow me wherever I shall lead you!"

Soon all the sled-dogs were sitting in a quiet circle
around their new leader.

"Good for you, Cheno!" said Kuni.

But as soon as he stretched out his hand
to show Cheno his feelings, the dog backed away
and growled. He did not want anyone to touch him.

When the time came for the family to go to sleep,
the boy placed fresh dishes of sealmeat and clear water
near the dog's corner in the house.

This time the dog drew closer. Kuni could see his nose
was quivering. Kuni kneeled down near the great dog
and spoke quietly to him.

"Cheno, I want to be good friends with you! I want you to be
part of our family. But you keep yourself so far away that you're
like a stranger!" The sharp, pointed ears moved slightly.
"I know that you'll do your work well as lead dog
on the sleds," said Kuni. "But I wish you could understand
that I want you to be my special friend too. Please try,
Cheno. Please." The husky watched quietly
as the boy waved goodnight and went off to sleep in his bed.

Outside under the dark Arctic sky, the cold winds
grew stronger and sharper. Soon the sounds
of the howling winds made their way into Kuni's dreams,
becoming evil-looking spirits howling and beckoning to him
with long, curved arms! Kuni tried to call out for help
but could only make a tiny noise. The next thing Kuni knew
was that he was being nudged by something cool.
It was Cheno's nose, and there was Cheno sitting by his bed.

"Oh, Cheno!" said Kuni. "Did I have a scary dream! But how did you know?"

The husky dog lifted his paw and gently placed it on Kuni's hand. The boy was delighted. He knew that Cheno was feeling like part of the family at last!

Kuni threw his arms around the dog's great head and buried his face in the long, thick fur around his throat. After a moment, Cheno began to lick Kuni, trying playfully to reach his ears!

The boy was so happy he could hardly speak. As he settled down for the rest of the night, the dog was there by his bed. Kuni looked down at him and whispered lovingly, "Goodnight, my Cheno— and thank you for your friendship, the best birthday gift of all!"

Children of the Yukon
by
Ted Harrison

As regular as winter, the ravens return
to the towns and villages of the Yukon
from their summer nesting places.
Noisy, bold and black against the snow,
they scatter garbage, tease dogs
and fight over food thrown to them
by the children.

From CHILDREN OF THE YUKON © 1977 Ted Harrison published by Tundra Books.

Winter and night come early to the Yukon.
In November, by mid-afternoon,
darkness has already fallen
on Dawson City and its ghost buildings.
Children make snowmen
on their way home from school;
soon the cold air will make the snow
too powdery for packing.

On Nares Lake at Carcross,
children haul water from ice holes
and play around the *S.S. Tutshi*,
a retired paddlewheeler that still watches
over the village from its resting place
on shore. It was one of many boats
that supplied northern communities in summer
carrying passengers and freight,
before roads were built.

The sound of dogs barking
and children laughing often means
a snowshoe race is taking place.
Running on snowshoes is difficult but fun.
Even beginners laugh at themselves
as they trip and tumble, and struggle
to get back upright.

In February, mushers
from all over the North bring their teams
of trained huskies to Whitehorse
for the "Yukon Sourdough Rendezvous."
The 75-kilometre race on the frozen
Yukon River is a reminder
of the days before roads and planes
when the dogsled and horse-drawn sleighs
were the only winter transportation.
Children cheer from the sidelines.

Fishing as well as trapping
goes on in winter.
Boys help fathers fish
through the ice on Crag Lake
near Carcross.

The snowshoe rabbit is snared
for food and fur—
to make mukluks and mittens.
A rabbit with large furry feet
that help it hop on snow,
it changes its coat
from brown in summer
to white in winter.

"Have you got your moose?"
is a common greeting during
the hunting season, for the lordly moose
still provides much meat for food,
leather for clothing and antlers for carving.
Successful hunters carry their trophy
home proudly, for the hunt has usually been
a hard one over rough wilderness.

There's a Sound in the Sea
A Child's-Eye View of the Whale
collected by
Tamar Griggs

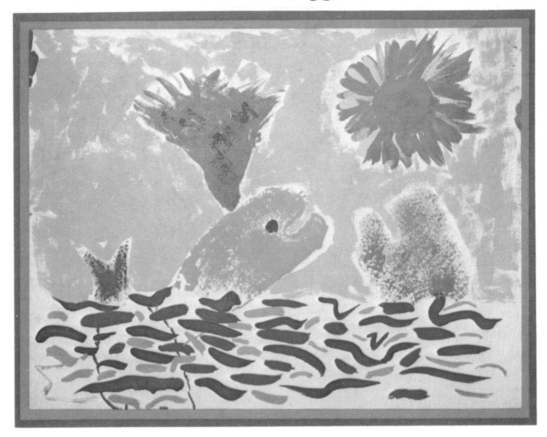

Stephen Wilder

Here come the whales!
Splashing their tails!
What a sight to see!
If only I could be a whale of the sea,
It would be fun, but I'm me.
                    Linda Pohwat

Jonathon Prosky

Silly and funny.
  Wet.
Friendly, fat, huge
  Nearsighted.
        Kirk Lombard

Alan Hicks

Swish, swish,
Blub, blub.
  It's dark and gloomy.
Blub, blub, blub, swish, swish.
  Sometimes it is very quiet.
Blub, blub, swish, swish, swish.
  But it is always my home.
                Judy Mitchell

Wyomina Park Elementary School

The men kill the whale.
They do not waste the great
whale,
Except its beauty.
            Margaret Rakas

Ann Norwick

The moonlight fell upon her head,
and the moon shone brightly
through the warm, dusty air.
The sea that had danced against the cliffs
was finally calm in the dead of night.
And then she blew,
which broke the silence
that echoed in
against the cliffs.

Laura Payne